Cigar Boys

Stories from the Ashes

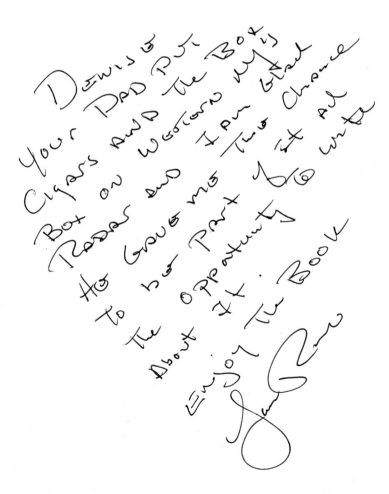

Cigar Boys

Stories from the Ashes

A Collection of Short Stories by Lou Rossi

FIVE COUNT
PUBLISHING
LLC

Library of Congress Control Number: 2015956868.

Printed and published in the United States by Five Count Publishing LLC.

www.fivecountpub.com.

ISBN 978-1-943706-03-7 (paperback)
ISBN 978-1-943706-04-4 (e-book)

Cover Design by Gwynn Olds.

I would like to thank all the guys at the Box whose great sense of humor and willingness to share allowed me to write this fun book of short stories. Most people, if they get out of this life with one or two good friends, they are lucky. I consider myself blessed to call many of you my close friends.

It is with honor, love, and privilege that I write these stories and thank each and every one of you for allowing me to call you friend.

Foreword

Note from the Editor of the *Box Burns Gazette.*

The *Box Burns Gazette* was created in order to document and share the stories of the patrons and employees at the Box, a local cigar shop. Why, you ask? We say, why not?

The goings-on at the Box and the trouble the loyal customers get into became just too much for us here at the *Gazette*. We couldn't help but share these brilliant yet idiotic tales. You will be introduced to many of the Box regulars. Below are just a few:

- Tom Gavigan – Successful financial expert who served our country and has a tendency to embellish or trivialize any story. Example: the Chicago Fire was a chance to lite up a cigar and barbeque the cow who kicked over the lantern.
- Jim Pauly – Expert home remodeler. If you want the best, Jim is the man to call. Besides being successful, he manages to make the three stooges' antics look normal. He finds himself in more jams than traffic in Los Angeles.
- John Crantzy – Landscaping is John's specialty and he owns one the most successful landscaping businesses in western New York. John manages to destroy the English language because he gets so excited

when he talks. He has a great fondness for his alma mater, *The* Ohio State University.

- Andre – Also known as the Terrorist. Andre can take it as well as dish it. He is Middle Eastern descent, he is generous, and true to his heritage, he is always looking for a deal.
- Dave Masin – A proud United States Marine. He served his country and we thank him for his service. He loves the Corp and he never lets anyone forget it. He has the memory of a twenty-year-old and there isn't a story he has forgotten. His luck when it comes to liquid is horrendous.
- Mr. Milanovich – His business is food and beverage. Mostly Beverage! A man who believes money rules and health is an afterthought.
- Sweet Lou – Late-night purveyor at the Box and the one guy who seems normal out of the bunch, which isn't saying much.
- Ron Wilson – Retired educator, religious commentator, and a very generous man who mantra is, "If it's on the internet it has to be true." Also known as Rooster.

We hope you enjoy all the shenanigans these yahoos get themselves into, because we at the *Box Burns Gazette* certainly enjoy reporting them.

Table of Contents

Cuban Cigar Crisis

The Cuban cigar embargo led Box officials to a midlevel cigar dealer, Ron Wilson, street name Rooster. Rooster was caught, according to an unreliable source, dealing a box of Cuban cigars at the Box. Box officials, along with, according to our unreliable source, the ATF (alcoholics, tobacconists, and firearms enthusiasts), swooped in and dismantled the cigar cartel with the use of a high-tech security system and a well-placed informant. Rooster was caught totally by surprise and was reprimanded severely.

According to the most unreliable source we could find, this penalty will be severe. The penalty for such an offense carries a maximum two-week fallen-ash vacuuming period.

As always with these cases, according to Box officials, the main man of the cartel gets away scot-free. However, *Gazette* informers tell this reporter that Box officials have a tip as to who the headman is. He is believed to be a former Syrian National and known bomb-making expert with ties to the Premier Liquor Empire. He is said to have a hairy back and shouts, "Allah Akbar" (sic). We believe this means "the cattle are dying" in Arabic.

Delivery Debacle

Prejudice reared its ugly head at the Box regarding an egregious case of blatant delivery prejudice. *Gazette* reporters witnessed this civil rights violation on, of all days, the Sabbath.

A Box customer known for landscaping and his love of *The Ohio State University* was in dire need of something for the tooth as his dearly beloved Buckeyes took it on the chin again in a big game. Pining for a Cannoli from the world famous Milanovich's Pizzeria, the Ohio State fan called the owner for a delivery of a cannoli. He was flatly refused. Mr. OSU stated that Mr. Milanovich said, and we quote here, "NO CANOLI FOR YOU."

"What a Nazi," Mr. OSU said in disgust.

In speaking with Mr. Milanovich, *Box Burns Gazette* learned the restaurant was closed and if that, "Poor excuse of a fan for a poor excuse of a team who couldn't beat the Little Sisters of the Poor wanted food he should have called when the pizzeria was open. This man will be late for his own funeral. That's probably for the best, since he is an OSU fan, they'll probably, as they do in all big games, choke and drop the casket." Harsh words from a well-known businessman.

Never one to give up, unlike his beloved OSU teams, he called Mr. Milanovich and asked him to drop by Wegmans and pick up a little dessert for him. Mr. OSU was shocked and dismayed at Milanovich's response, which was, "ARE YOU ON FUCKING CRACK."

Box Burns reporters learned Mr. Milanovich has no problem delivering at all hours of the night to a well-known construction magnate known for buying his wife of many years a new white Mercedes convertible. Can you say discrimination?

When asked, Milanovich responded, "I hate OSU," and, "Mr. New White Mercedes tips better."

The Box tried to get a quote from Mr. Mercedes, but he said no comment, because, "If my wife finds out I'm tipping she'll want a new Bentley."

The Box also spoke to Mr. OSU and when told of these clan-destine deliveries, had one thing to say to Mr. Milanovich, "NO MULCH FOR YOU."

Spill Spurs Major Rug Cleaning

Box Burns Gazette has learned that a catastrophic spill at the Box has spurred a major rug cleaning.

EPA agents were on the scene of a spill which made the Exxon Valdese and BP oil spills seem like a dripping faucet. A customer known only as Blinky is under investigation. This *Gazette* reporter has learned that this customer is known for numerous stories, repeated joke telling, and deafness. He has spilled more drinks than an epileptic holding a jug of water while having a seizure.

Box officials discovered a lake under the carpet and are now having it drained and the rug cleaned.

Also, the Box, the EPA, and the Tobacco Lobby will institute a fine for further spillage.

Acer Caper

Let the buyer beware has never been truer as one long-time Box customer has learned.

The unnamed victim known to frequent a local drinking establishment called Alternative Brews on a daily basis was trying to enhance his schooling by purchasing a computer. An unnamed seller told him that he had a computer for sale that was hardly used for three-hundred dollars. It sounded like a great deal, and as we all know, what sounds to be good to be true often is. Well, as you can imagine, it took less time to read *War and Peace* in Russian than it did to start his "new computer."

The buyer told a friend of his at the Box about his plight. The friend, who shall remain unnamed but goes by the moniker Sweetness, was incensed. He began to investigate this purchase and discovered many irregularities. The computer was found to have 1,400 viruses and two illegal programs on it. He had a computer expert look at it. This expert, also a former Syrian National bomb maker and entrepreneur, discovered the mishaps.

He cleaned up the computer and got the buyer settled down.

The seller, much to his chagrin, was outraged at such a claim and took to the offensive. He threatened to sue Box officials and Sweetness for character assassination, which proved to be baseless. The seller demanded an apology in front of three unknown, unreliable, unattainable, and unbelievable witnesses. He showed up at the Box with a microcassette recorder to get his apology from Sweetness. As you can guess, Sweetness was galled at the thought of this. But to keep the peace, he gave an apology.

The seller, believe it or not, wants to be just one of the guys again and offered the buyer a two-hundred-dollar lifetime subscription to Cigar Snob magazine.

Stay tuned for the seller reaction in next month's *Box Burns Gazette*.

Failed Quest

For a person to become successful in life you have to have determination and a never-give-up attitude. However, no matter how determined one can be and no matter the amount of never-give-up is in that person, sometimes you just aren't successful at what you are trying to achieve.

This happened to one Box regular as he tried to find his favorite beverage at a sporting event.

On a beautiful summer day in the Rockies, Box regular Jimmy "Big Rig" Pauly took his family to a Major League Baseball game at Coors Field in Denver, Colorado.

The stadium was beautiful and the atmosphere at the ball park was great, but Big Rig had one complaint: "They don't serve Budweiser at Coors Field and that's bullshit."

Big Rig walked in and he and his family sat in the concourse area waiting for the game to start. He asked his family if they were thirsty. They all placed their order with Jim and he left to procure the drinks.

He got to the concession stand serving the area where his family was sitting, waited in line for ten minutes, and placed his order. "I'll have three Coors and a Bud." The server looked at Jim puzzled and asked him to repeat his order.

Jim did, and the server replied, "Sir, we only serve Coors here." Jim was getting pissed and told the server don't worry about it, he'll try another stand. The server shook his head.

Jim went back to the seats and told his family he has to go to another stand to get a Bud. Before his family could stop him Big Rig was gone.

Jim wandered the stadium for another stand. He found one and waited in line another ten minutes and placed his order. "I'll take three Coors and Bud."

"Sir, we don't serve Bud here. How about a Coors?"

"No, I want a Bud and I'll get a Bud. I'll go to another stand."

This went on for seven innings. Big Rig's family still hadn't had anything to drink in hours and became dehydrated. Finally, as he wandered the stadium, he ran into Mr. Coors. Jim recognized him from the TV commercials, stopped him in the concourse, introduced himself, and began to scream at him. "Mr. Coors, how in the hell can you put your name on this beautiful stadium and not serve America's beer?"

Mr. Coors immediately gave Big Rig a confused look and pointed to the humongous sign that clearly spelled out "COORS FIELD."

Big Rig's response, "Oh! I'll take four Coors, please!"

God forbid this guy goes to Coca Cola Field, the Pepsi Center, or Busch Stadium. I think he'll do okay at Busch; the others, I'm not so sure.

Reality Shows Visit Box Customer

Box officials confirm a Hollywood Access report that reality show producers from *Hoarders*, *Pawn Stars*, and *American Pickers* visited the home of a Box regular sometime last week.

Gazette reporters were on hand with the reality show producers when they visited the humble abode of Jimmy "the Rug" Palisano. The look of sheer astonishment on their faces was priceless. One producer was quoted, "I've never seen such treasures," as he viewed the hordes of napkins the Rug has collected over the years.

The producers looked like kids waiting to see what was under the tree at Christmas. The Rug was only too happy to have them scour his home for hidden gems.

What they found was amazing. As you walk in your senses are immediately overwhelmed at the sea of white. That's right, wall-to-wall napkin carpeting and wallpaper. But that, folks, is only the beginning, as the Rug, aka Captain Napkin, allowed producers to walk through his home.

Jimmy was not fazed at all by the attention and only had one request: that no camera lights be used, since his home is highly flammable and the intense heat from the lights would not only set his collection on fire, but his home as well. The Rug explained he had to have a Halon fire suppression system put in just in case of a fire, plus all his heat and smoke detectors had to be hardwired right to Amherst Fire Control and to the Amherst Police.

Jimmy told the producers to look for themselves and not to touch anything because he could not be disturbed. Jimmy was eating a seven-course Milanovich meal in front of his 1952 RCA television watching a rerun of a Yankee game from 1973. One producer was quoted, "That man eats like he's going to the electric chair and from the sounds he makes I'd pull the switch myself."

The tour began with his coffee table made out of napkin dispensers collected over the years, ranging from 1942 to the present. Asked how he got them, Jimmy replied, "I have jeans specially made from the Andy Cook Collection lined with flannel and specially installed deep pockets which allow for the strategic placement of the dispensers as I leave the restaurants."

Next stop, Jimmy's bedroom. Why, you ask? The answer: napkin sheets and pillows. Move over, Sealy Posturepedic. However, that is only a tease of what is yet to come.

The den is where the real eighth wonder of the world is. Jimmy, in his spare time, has created – all out of napkins, mind you – life-sized statues of his heroes. The list is long and distinguished. It includes statues of Babe Ruth, Joe DiMaggio, Yogi Berra, Whitey Ford, "The Mick" Mickey Mantle, Don Mattingly, and modern-day star Derrick Jeter. Jimmy is currently working on a napkin replica of the famed House that Ruth Built, Yankee Stadium.

As Jimmy was working on his current project, a napkin toupee, he was heard saying, "How do I keep it dry when I go swimming?" The producers were quite sure he would figure it out.

Jimmy has each napkin numbered and catalogued on a specially designed computer that cost three-hundred dollars, purchased from an unnamed computer retailer operating out of the Box.

The piece de résistance was yet to come. Locked inside a hermetically sealed glass vault was the napkin used by Jesus at the last supper, Marie Antoinette of let them eat cake fame, and Jimmy's first ever napkin. Let the bidding begin. Also in the vault were the napkin dispensers from the movie *American Graffiti*, *The Godfather* where Michael Corleone shot the Police Captain, Sparks Restaurant where mafia boss Paul Castellano was shot, as well as local eating establishments Chefs, Milanovich's, and Mulberry's.

Still, nothing fazed Jimmy as he rounded third and headed for dessert, which consisted of a homemade cherry pie from the oven of nursery magnate John Crantzy's mother and Wegmans French Vanilla Ice Cream. Jimmy was quoted, "I can't wait 'til tomorrow night's dinners at Ulrich's, they have a great German dispenser that says 'Hiel Hitler' as you take a napkin from it." This reporter is quite sure it will wind up in the vault as well.

As we headed to the garage another surprise awaited us. We discovered Jimmy is not only a designer, but an automotive engineer as well. Jimmy stated he needs a new car because his current model, a 1957 Edsel, has ten miles on it. Jimmy is making a 2011 Mercedes Benz out of Bounty paper towels gathered from various food stores throughout Germany, complete with napkin air bags. I can't wait to see that on showroom floors.

Well, it was an exhausting tour of napkin marvels. And speaking of marvels, Marvel Comic Books has contracted Jimmy to make life-sized action figures of Spiderman, the Hulk, Ironman, and Captain America. Marvel said they would supply the napkins, but Jimmy insisted he would get them if Marvel picked up the meal tab. Can you say bankrupt? We will keep you posted on Jimmy and all his latest projects, or you can look for yourself at Jimmy's website, captainnapkin.com.

A fight broke out between the producers of *Pawn Stars* and *American Pickers* as to who would get first shot at airing this napkin masterpiece. *Gazette* reporters were able to calm things down by saying there are plenty of napkins to go around.

Also, readers, if you wonder why prices at restaurants are higher locally than the national average, look no further than the Rug's Napkin Cave and you'll know the answer. And if you are ever short of napkins, do not ask the Rug, use your sleeve.

The *Box Burns Gazette* will keep you informed when the show will air. So get your DVRs ready for these can't-miss, heart-stopping episodes.

Box Opens Apothecary

Box owners tell the *Gazette* they are branching out into the pharmacology field by opening a medieval Apothecary to offset the financial woes created by the New York State tax placed on all tobacco products.

Box officials say they are entering this endeavor with two well-known Box medieval pharmacists, Ron "Theodoric of York" Wilson and Tom "Elva Edison" Gavigan. Their motto: there is nothing that can't be cured without hydrogen peroxide. They also deliver using Amish couriers with the slogan, "A teaspoon of peroxide, the new fountain of youth" painted on the side of their horses.

That's right, readers, all your ailments will be cured. This modern-day medieval pharmacy will be stocked with all the latest high-tech pharmaceuticals, such as roots, berries, potions, and their secret weapon, thirty-four percent medical-grade hydrogen peroxide. Also, a super computer purchased at the Box Computing Center run by an unknown businessman already equipped with viruses and registry errors and manned by a Syrian Nationalist will be used to fill your peroxide prescriptions.

Here is a list of their cures:

- Nose Bleed – tea bag, strawberries, and hydrogen peroxide.

- Psoriasis – coconut oil and hydrogen peroxide.
- Melanoma – coconut oil and hydrogen peroxide.
- Skin Cancer – coconut oil and hydrogen peroxide.
- Amputations – coconut oil and hydrogen peroxide.
- Baldness – coconut oil and hydrogen peroxide.
- Knee and hip Replacements – thing of the past, all you need is an injection of licorice, coconut oil, and hydrogen peroxide.
- Tendinitis – injection of licorice, coconut oil, and hydrogen peroxide.
- Tonsillitis – this, folks, is truly amazing, you actually drink hydrogen peroxide, not the stuff you buy in store, but through the Internet.
- Death – Coconut oil, dandelion root, licorice, and, of course, HYDROGEN PEROXIDE.

These cures are truly a miracle. I quote Theodoric of York, "Who needs doctors when we can solve all your woes with peroxide?" Also, get ten percent off with a purchase of a cigar at the Box. This deal excludes all purchases of Cuban cigars.

Although independent pharmacies have set up protests to stop the opening of the Apothecary, Box Officials will continue with the project, stating, "We cannot be stopped."

Grand opening is expected in two weeks. Stay tuned, readers.

Fashion Faux Pas Flabbergasts Box Patrons

Box customers were astounded by the fashion faux pas that struck during the Sabres seventh game of the NHL Playoffs Wednesday night.

As patrons entered the famed smoke shop, they were awe struck by the fashion statement made by a long-time Box customer. Regulars are used to seeing famed fashion statements made by the likes of the Andy Cook Collection so proudly worn by Jimmy the Rug, the Ohio State Collection, the Park Country Club montage of gear worn by a former covert ops serviceman, the Sweet Lou Argyle Clothing Line, the pink attire sported by Bob Rakoczy and staff, and the famed Jim Pauly Line.

However, no one was prepared for this look put together by the world's historian Dave "I mention every name unknown to all mankind or that no one cares about" Masin. Mr. Masin strutted about the Box wearing a sleeveless Raiders jersey accented by non-matching sweatpants and sneakers.

Box customers told the *Gazette* he normally tops off this gear with combat boots purchased at an unknown PX at some top secret Marine base. Box supporters were amazed at the site of the mini guns and the worn-out Globe and Anchor Tattoo that now resembles a marble and fishhook.

One Box customer known for breaking up a Hawaiian drug cartel offered some sage advice for this hard-working Box fashion statement: "There are two things you can do with that shirt.

First, you can wash your car with it, or second, set it on fire." No arguments from this reporter.

Box Burns Gazette decided to look into the matter further and consulted a fashion expert, that being THE LATE MR. BLACKWELL. After finally getting through to THE LATE MR. BLACKWELL and showing him a photo of the clothing worn by Mr. "did I ever tell about my 1964 GTO" Masin, THE LATE MR. BLACKWELL exclaimed, "I'm glad I'm dead."

Blackwell went on to create a new Top Ten worst dressed workout gear list:

1. The Raider collection by Mr. Masin
2. Hans and Franz
3. Charlie Brown
4. Beaver Cleaver
5. Jack "LA" lane
6. Jared the Subway Guy
7. Uncle Fester
8. Richard Simmons
9. Oprah Winfrey
10. Spanky Spankowitz

As a result of this faux pas, Box Officials are now placing signs throughout the store banning all sleeveless shirts and requiring the purchase of a five-dollar cigar.

Until next time, WEAR SLEEVES.

What Would Bond DO!!!!!

James Bond at the Box, yes, folks, it's true. The *Box Burns Gazette* has learned a real-life James Bond does thrive at the Box. The covert spy does truly exist.

According to unreliable and unknown sources, this Bond non-look alike has nothing in common at all with James Bond. As a matter of fact, he has more in common with Gold Bond than James Bond. Also, according to these very unreliable sources, Leprechauns wait for him to show up so they can stand behind him in line at the adult rides and get on.

This unnamed boisterous customer gets himself into more jams than Lucy, Ricky, Fred, and Ethel, but unlike this cast of misfits, our Bond "Gets away with murder," to quote Lindy Ruff of Sabres fame.

Based on information gathered by a very close but truly undependable source, *Box Burns* reporters learned this is possible due to his extensive training as an undercover lifeguard in the Army, a Navy Seal, an Air Force Para Rescue Man, and a Coast Guard Rescue Swimmer. He single handedly saved the crew of the Crab Boat Northwestern from drowning in the Bering Sea, broke up a Hawaiian drug ring, successfully mediated the After Hours Crisis of 2010, and saved the Box from sleeveless shirts.

However, his luck took a tragic turn one day at a Syrian National Stag Party, which actually turned out to be a fundraiser for Al-Qaeda dental care. This modern-day Bond tried to smoke one of his Cuban cigars bought from his Cuban cigar connection and was told there was no smoking. He went nuts and was heard saying, "What do you mean no smoking? You allow these people, who by the way they stink to high heaven, to bring in their goats, and I can't smoke a cigar? Bullshit."

Well, let the party begin. As he was eating, of all things, a ham sandwich at an all Al-Qaeda event, the goat shit hit the fan and a slap fest broke out along with all types of weaponry provided to them by the Masin Arms Company. A burqa-clad Al-Qaeda woman warrior slapped our James Bond in the face and his right incisor was knocked clean out his mouth. This incensed Bond to no end and he got into his ninja stance and was heard saying, "When I get done with you, you'll feel like you've been surrounded." She immediately slapped him again and almost cost him another tooth.

Our wayward warrior called the Buffalo Police and seven cars and a Police Lieutenant showed up along with a former high-ranking police official and had the place shut down in twenty minutes. How is that for quick action?

The next day, after looking in the mirror and seeing that his tooth had been slapped out of him, he called his Syrian dental connection to see if he could get a new tooth put in. The Syrian immediately called all his secret dental friends who work with covert cigar smokers and had the latest in tooth replacement for spies put in. This dentist, believe it or not, put in a BLUE TOOTH, so this covert customer can now read, drink coffee, smoke, and talk on the phone while driving his car. If only they could teach him change a tire or buy his own AAA.

Where is my 8-Track-Playing Tractor?

A Well-known construction baron and clothing designer made short-term-memory-loss patients feel good about themselves.

In an attempt to relive his youth, this construction magnate went to extreme measures to proliferate ANY AND ALL 8-track tapes left in America to play in his tractor and grow a retro porn star mustache. To put his diabolical plan in motion, he hired a Middle Eastern Militia non-com to do his bidding. He instructed his 8-track-searching mercenary to use any all means to find these priceless relics of the past and to pay any amount in the world, as long as it wasn't more than thirty dollars.

The unknown Syrian diligently obeyed his master, for he knew at the end of this perilous journey what would be his final reward, which, according to his religious beliefs, was an end-of-the-month statement on his PayPal account. The Syrian scoured all the lists – Craigslist, Penney Saver, Metro Community News, Syrian Swap Sheet, and all Middle Eastern Ali Baba Bazaars – to no avail. Frustration began to build and it looked like the Syrian Sherpa would pull the rip cord on his newly tailored, Andy-Cook-designed denim dynamite vest.

It finally hit him as he began to smoke his Cuban cigar, bought from an unknown cigar dealer in town: EBAY. Mission accomplished. He completed his quest and delivered the tapes to the home improvement king. The king rewarded his Sherpa with a rarity, a Cuban cigar bought from a midlevel cigar dealer known as Rooster. Unbeknownst to the king, he gave his Sherpa his own cigar back.

Well, the construction magnate, after consuming a week's worth of Milanovich meals in one sitting, headed down to his compound in Franklinville. Looking like the cat that ate the canary, or in this case put Milanovich's out business, he began to look for his precious 8-track-playing tractor.

He searched one tractor, then another, then another tractor. He checked them all, right down to the Oliver Wendle Douglas tractor which had no engine, much less an 8-track player. He called to his faithful companion Jesse, "Have you seen my 8-track player?" To which Jesse replied, "No, I'm busy washing your white Mercedes convertible that is supposed to be in Florida, and it doesn't have an 8-track either."

Finally, it struck the home improvement king; none of his tractors had an 8-track player in them from the start. The worst part is he still has the retro mustache!

Barista Burned at the Box

"Oh the humanity" was heard throughout the Box when an employee suffered a near fatal burn to his right hand on Saturday. The *Box Burns Gazette* learned the Box employee, an unidentified male named Charlie who wished to remain anonymous, was the injured party. The *Gazette* was able to get an exclusive with the maimed employee.

Charlie stated he was waiting on two Twin City Paramedics when in walked Dave "Shaky Hand" Masin. "I was extremely busy that day due to the fact that my partner was involved in the Manchester United vs. Real Madrid soccer Match. Shaky Hand walked up to the counter and ordered a coffee, black."

Charlie told this *Gazette* writer, and I quote, "This Minga can't even figure out that I'm fucking busy, much less tie those frigging combat boots when he works out. Stunod! So I get the coffee and Masin throws the dollar on the register and thus begins the nightmare."

Shaky Hand grabbed the coffee in the Styrofoam cup and pulled out his mug with the Sippy top and began to pour boiling coffee from the cup to the mug. Shaking like a Parkinson patient in an earthquake, Masin missed the mug, and like lava erupting from Mt. Vesuvius, coffee rained down on poor Charlie's right hand, causing life-threatening injuries. As the coffee cascaded off the counter, the spill raised to flood levels and headed toward the lounge.

The two paramedics were stunned; they had never seen such an act of clumsiness. They rushed to poor Charlie and were heard saying "Oh my God, the humanity, we've never seen such a burn on a human before." They sprinted to the Apothecary next door and grabbed the only thing that could save poor Charlie's hand, a mixture of coconut oil and thirty-four percent hydrogen peroxide.

They rushed the burned barista to Millard Fillmore Hospital. *Gazette* Reporters caught up with the punctual paramedics and asked how they happened to be in the Box.

One of the medics, Spunky Spankowitz of the famous Spankowitz clan, gave a statement:

> All we wanted to do was buy a cigar and leave when this customer came in, told us thank you for your service, ordered the coffee, and began telling us about the time President Kennedy waved to him from the middle of the ocean while he was making napalm. We then saw him try to pour coffee into a mug and all hell broke loose, because while trying to pour coffee from one cup to the next he began to tell us about his 1964 GTO. The next thing we know an old man is screaming and there was coffee everywhere.

The injuries sustained by Charlie were third-degree burns to his right hand and his friends now call him LEFTY.

However, the story does not end there. There was so much coffee spilled that it caused wide-spread devastation to the lounge. The rouge coffee wave, which made the Japanese tsunami look like a ripple in the water, threw chairs everywhere, flooded the humidors, and worst all, shorted out the electrical, thus wiping out the soccer pay-per-view event paid for by a well-hidden second Box employee. Customers were fighting for their lives as they clung to bits of broken furniture to stay afloat until help could arrive.

That help came in the form of a former undercover lifeguard of the Army (Ret.) who jumped in and pulled the customers to safety.

As a result, the Box was declared a disaster Area and FEMA was called in. Mr. Masin can no longer have liquids and all cigars are officially declared over-humidified.

Pond Predicament

A pond given as a gift for Father's Day has gone horribly wrong, *Box Burns Gazette* has learned.

The pond owner, a former Undercover Christmas Seal, became perplexed and obsessed by the sudden drop in the water level.

The out-of-sync ex-Seal began to ponder the pond's problem on his own, but just could not figure it out. An idea struck him. "I'll go to the Box and somebody there will know the answer to this perplexing problem."

As the pond owner entered the Box looking for an answer to his dilemma, he came across construction king Jim Pauly of porn mustache and missing-8-track-player fame. He described his conundrum in complete detail, obsessing on every point. Jim began to stroke his mustache, thinking he wished he had an 8-track player in his tractor, and, after giving no consideration to the problem, turned to the proud pond owner and exclaimed, "You have a hole in it."

The pissed pond owner, looking like someone just told him to put a lid on his Park Club Coffee container, screamed, "Are you fucking kidding me! You build million-dollar homes and this is the best you can come up with? By the way, I have a leak in my roof, can you tell what's wrong with it?"

Again, Mr. Pauly pondered the vexing leak situation and replied, "You have a hole in it."

The problematic pond owner next turned to John Crantzy, a local nursery magnate. "Hey, Crantzy, can you come down to my house and look at my pond, the water level keeps getting low, I'll buy the doughnuts and take you to the Park Club for coffee, your treat."

Crantzy looked at the troubled pond prince and replied, "Yeah, you have a hole in it."

The pissed pond owner yelled again, "Are you fucking kidding me! And by the way, can you landscape my roof?"

Frustrated by the simplistic answers he was receiving, he turned too recently landed Jim Blount. The concrete company owner, who operates his Buffalo business from Florida, perused the problem, checked his ticket for his flight back to Florida, then told the pugilistic pond owner, "You know what your problem is?"

The owner replied, "If I did would I ask you? What the fuck. What is the problem?"

Jim replied, "Yeah, you have a hole in it."

The pugnacious pond owner screamed again "Are you fucking kidding me!"

The perplexed, pissed, and puzzled pond owner ran into a sleeveless, '70s-shorts-and-combat-boot-wearing Dave Masin and explained his plight to him. Dave thought about the issue, spilled his coffee – burning poor Charlie again – rubbed his marble, fishhook, and scarecrow tattoo and pontificated, "I remember driving in my 1964 GTO, which I paid 1,965 dollars for, with my buddy Frank Tully, who played running back for Holy Cross and who could dance up a storm and was a general manager for a car dealership in Boston, down the NY State Thruway at mile marker 237 on my way to see my French Canadian father-in-law with a 1942 Garand sniper rifle in the trunk, about his pond problem. Tom, Tom, Tom are you listening?"

The frustrated pond owner replied, "Will you get to the fucking point!"

"Well, Tom, it was 1966 and the Vietnam War was raging, and you know what his problem was?"

"No! What was the problem, dammit?" the pond owner yelled.

Dave leaned over to Tom and said, "He had a hole in it!"

Sensing no relief for his problem, the pond owner turned to a cartoon drawing, midlevel Cuban cigar dealer named Rooster. Rooster thought about the poor pond owner's situation and drew the answer of a Styrofoam cup. He drew Tom with a Seal float wrapped around him, standing in eighteen inches of water up to his neck, with the end of the pond marked deep end and an arrow pointing to the wall of the pond. The caption read, "YOU HAVE A HOLE IN IT!"

The pond owner, reduced to tears, cried out, "I'm going home to watch *Dancing with the Stars!*"

Sleeper-Cell Compound

What was thought to be an ordinary turkey hunt and clam-bake turned out to be a twisted nightmare for this construction magnate and Pauly Pavilion compound owner.

Trying to build up Islamic relations – or non-Islamic relations, whomever you believe – compound owner Jim "I never seen this coming" Pauly brought a lonely, unknown, unreliable, and green-card-carrying Syrian National to his quaint and quiet Franklinville compound to show him what a green, wooded area with water looks like.

Unbeknownst to Mr. Pauly, this devilishly tricky Syrian was carrying a hidden camera in his camel-skin flask to take photos of the area, as well as other assorted items which were well hidden in white robes.

Jim describes the scene as chaotic that next morning:

We got up early to go turkey hunting, I asked my guest if he would like to try one of my guns. He said, 'no I brought my own.' I began to scratch my retro mustache and thought I heard a lot of strange noises last night, but I thought it was a goose trying to get laid. So I fell back asleep. So after saying that he brought his own gun, I pulled back the pink curtains my wife made for the man-cave and my heart sank. There it was, my 1937 Allis–Chalmers orange tractor on the front lawn with an 80-

millimeter cannon strapped on it. I was stunned. I was thankful my wife's Mercedes wasn't here, she would have killed me. I kept wondering why he kept asking me if I had a pickup with an extended bed in the back here. NOW I KNOW.

After convincing the Syrian National the cannon, white robe, and turban could not be used for hunting, the Syrian pulled out a ghillie suit that snipers wear and an AK-47. Well, according to witnesses, he looked like either a hairy yeti or a big hedge in a Scottish moor. One witness claimed to have seen Sherlock Holmes coming from the hedge with Dr. Watson. Needless to say, there were no turkeys shot that day.

Then off to the clam bake where plenty of Bud was drank and clams eaten. The Syrian was upset and was heard to yell, "AL-LAH ALLAH YIPE YIPE Yi Yi ALLAH," which means, "WHAT, NO GOAT?" Also, Mr. Pauly had to keep the townspeople away from the uninvited guest because they kept wanting to shave his back and make a sweater. Mr. Pauly had to tell them it's not wool.

As the weekend came to a close the home improvement king woke up to the sounds of AK-47s being shot in the air. He looked outside and saw miles and miles of tents, sand, and palm trees. During the evening thousands of yards of sand and palm trees were shipped in from a well-unknown nursery in Clarence, making the Sahara Desert look like an oasis. The nursery owner was heard yelling, "Yeah, yeah, yeah, sales are up this week; I need something for my tooth."

Mr. Pauly was so stressed that he only shaved half of his 'stache off and his right eye began to blink. "We all thought he was sending Morse code," his caretaker Jesse exclaimed. There was yelling, screaming, shots being fired in the air, goats, and signs saying "bomb making next right," camels new and used, women with beards, and Osama sightings all over the little town of Franklinville. Jim asked his uninvited, unknown, unreliable, and unlikable guest how long his relatives would be staying. He replied, "Only a short while, maybe six to seven hundred years." Mr. Pauly was heard crying, "All this for a lousy Cuban cigar."

The construction magnate's woes did not end there. The EPA came in and closed down the compound due to the large amounts of lead on the grounds. Also, the FBI Joint Terrorism Task Force had the place surrounded. Can you say FOR SALE?

On a totally unrelated note, this well-known home improvement king, who wishes to remain unknown, will be flying to Florida to drive home his bride. This unknown well-known magnate told this *Gazette* reporter under no circumstances would he be driving his wife home from Florida. Again, let's all be thankful that he is not a bookie.

Masin Jeopardy Makes Box Debut

Box Burns Gazette has learned a new game show will make its debut at the Box called Masin Jeopardy. The show is named after one of the Boxes' all-time great storytellers, Dave Masin. Mr. Masin (who has regaled customers of the Box for years with his stories) will now be made famous.

No detail is too small for Dave. If it's non-essential, it's in the story. If you've never heard of the person and the name has no bearing on the story, it's in the story. As an added bonus, no non-essential dates, times, or places are left out the story.

Now you can play along. Here's how.

Every category will contain a question from the Masin Files and you will be able to tell your answer to the person next to you, who could give a crap. The idea is to call his or her name at least three times to get their attention and make sure they hear the answer you have given. The trick, however, is to make sure they have heard the answer at least five times. Anything less than five times constitutes a wrong answer.

The categories are:

- Napalm
- Marine Corps History
- Marine Weaponry
- Marine Vehicles

- Paris Island
- Vehicles
- Old School Mates
- Work History
- French Canadian Tales
- Major Box Spills

And many more that I can't possibly come up with. With each correct answer, you win nothing but the privilege of saying "I've heard that before."

One Box customer had so much fun playing that he was quoted as saying to Dave, "I've heard every story you've ever told and every name, place, and time that meant nothing to the story, and now that you have a good story you can't tell me the person's name. How fucked up is that?"

Well, Box customers, the moment you have all waited for. The question is, what was Dave's first car?

Good Luck.

Former Nixon Aide Denies Allegations

In true Nixon form, a former Nixon campaign worker denies any allegations of a leak that sprang from his head. This Box customer, who wishes to remain anonymous and would only say on the record that he loves *Dancing with the Stars* and *Desperate Housewives*, denies the fabrication of an unknown substance spewing from his head.

The *Gazette* has it on unreliable sources that this gusher could be seen in an area covering seven counties. One Box customer, who travels extensively throughout the USA, was quoted saying, "It made Old Faithful seem like a shower spray."

The *Dancing with the Stars* enthusiast denies any such wrongdoing; unfortunately for him, this *Gazette* reporter knows where to find a story.

The *Box Burns Gazette* turned up these little tidbits. While traveling with a well-known Ohio State Alum looking for a pond-replacement kit, a leak sprang from the head of the perplexed pond owner. The eruption was so loud and ghastly that it caused the OSU alum to squeeze the sandwich he was eating so hard that the mayo shot out and hit and him in the eye. The temporary blindness caused him to swerve off the road, hitting a flock of grounded birds. The birds were grounded due to the fact that they had lids from the Park Country Club impaled on their beaks. The SPCA is now investigating the Park Club and an unknown member.

This, folks, is only the beginning. Again denying the allega-
tion of leakage coming from the mountainous pimple on the side
of his head, the unknown Box customer, going against the advice
of his lawyer, Mr. Michael Iacano, the well-known Lexus Lawyer
whose motto is "I come to you because I have too," stated, "It's a
hydrogen peroxide mix I put on my head to shrink this pimple."
Mr. Iacano, unable to control his client, immediately picked him
up and put him in his office and drove away.

However, it was too late, as an astounded group of Box customers felt the Box quake, witnessed the horror of all drinks spilling onto the newly cleaned carpets – giving one shaky-hand customer an alibi for the first time in his Box career – and cigars
falling off the shelves as the growth on the side of this accused
customer's head ruptured, spewing a hydrogen peroxide and coconut oil mix the likes of which has never been seen from any
human being. There was peroxide everywhere.

Two Celebrities were in the box at the time. A Mrs. Butter-
worth and Aunt Jemima were heard screaming, "If only that boy
were a maple tree, we would have enough maple sap for a lifetime, Lordy, Lordy, Lordy."

The spill was so large that executives from BP Oil were called
in to assess the damage and to try and contain it. Emergency
crews immediately constructed an oil derrick on the side of the
falsely accused customer's head to cap the well. Large skimmers
were brought in to suck up the spill and contain any additional
damage.

While watching *CNN, Fox News*, and the *Gazette Cable
News*, the former Exxon Valdez Captain hired the Lexus Lawyer,
one Michael Iacano, to get his case overturned in the Supreme
Court. Iacano was quoted, "Even though I represent the falsely
accused in this case, I cannot turn my back or my car on justice.
This spill makes the Exxon Valdez spill look like a puddle. We
will prevail."

The *Gazette* also learned that Iacano represents Tennessee Titans Owner Bud Adams in Supreme Court in a suit to be brought against the falsely accused Box Customer. Iacano stated, "Mr. Adams placed an oil derrick on his team's helmets long before he put one on his head."

While admitting nothing, this unknown Box customer was heard to say, and we quote, "I may have overdone the peroxide this time, and by the way, did anyone catch *Desperate Housewives* Sunday?"

Lexus Lawyer in the Driver's Seat

A former Spiegel, Keller, and you've been Conned attorney staged a daring late-night raid on his former law offices.

Inspired by U.S. Navy Seal Team Six, Mr. Mike Iacano put together his own covert team. The team, now known as Non-Seal Team 1.5, consisting of a former Army lifeguard, former Marine Corporal, former Army Artillery Captain, present Syrian terrorist, and a former Navy Commander, was given its objective. The objective: Extract and return client files to the new office of Mr. Iacano.

The mission got off to a rough start as the group could not decide on calls signs. They tried colors but some could not decide on what shade, what type of masks to use, or whether to dress in black or white outfits for the mission.

The group decided to forgo the use of GPS and use the navigational skills of the ex-Army Captain and, as expected, they got lost because he brought napkins instead of a map. The Navy Commander bailed out because Manchester United was playing Arsenal for the tenth time.

Then the unexpected took place. The Syrian created an explosive mixture to blow the doors. He gave the mixture to the former Marine Corporal who promptly spilled it in to the city's sewer system and blew it kingdom come.

The Army lifeguard could only say, "Are you fucking kidding me! And by the way, did you know I have a hole in my pond?"

The frustrated attorney said, "Forget it, guys," and pulled out his key and took the files with him all in five minutes.

The despondent attorney decided to open a branch office at the Box. He put out his shingle on his recently rented locker where he now kept his files and coffee maker. His first client was a well-known nursery owner. They scheduled a time to meet at the Box. Again, things went horribly wrong. The nursery owner was late and so was Mr. Iacano. They tried again and this time neither showed up.

Frustrated by the situation, an after-hours shopkeeper known as Sweet Lou, and also known for his Argyle collection and hatred for Ohio State, suggested he work from his Lexus. Iacano pondered this new idea and went for it. He cleaned the McDonalds' wrappers from his car and Fabreezed the hell out of it to get rid of the cigar smell.

Finally, he was proud of his new office; it was spacious, room for five, which allowed him to give discounts to clients because he could now work with four at one time.

The conveniences were amazing; fine Corinthian leather for client comfort, a Sirius radio for clients waiting in the back seat for their appointment, coffee served at anytime and anywhere there is a drive-through, and for that special client, a drive-through Starbucks. The topper is the hermetically sealed trunk in which all files are kept.

Fees and rates are a thing of the past. Mr. Iacano charges by the mile instead of the hour and passes the savings on to you. No more business cards, he gives you his license plate number. No secretary because he uses a microcassette tape recorder purchased from a vendor who specializes in virus-equipped computers. Again, the savings are passed to you, the client.

The best part is you are never late for an appointment or court. Why, you ask? The answer is he picks you up! How is that for service?

Mr. Iacano has two mottos: I come to you because I have to, and you're never too far because I work out of my car.

Remember, folks, look for his plate, "LXS LWYR."

Cirque de la Horton's

How does breakfast become an adventure? Good question. Just ask Oscar Madison and Felix Unger of the Box, or better known as John Crantzy and Tom Gavigan. The Box's version of the odd couple decided after discussing the landscaping to be done at the residence of one Tom "I have a hole in my pond" Gavigan they would go out for coffee and John would treat.

Sick of seeing Tom walking around with an empty Park Club coffee cup, and just basically sick of the Club all together, he talked the malcontent member into going to Horton's for coffee.

Unbeknownst to Mr. Crantzy, a highly slippery sealant was put on Tom's new concrete work. John somehow got the sealant on his shoe and was unaware of the danger that would befall him.

As the two entered Horton's arguing about whether or not a birch tree would look good on the roof, the world as John Crantzy knew it would end. Two minutes before the dynamic duo entered the coffee shop, one David Masin was leaving. Mr. Masin secured a black coffee in a spill-proof mug, (we all know how well that works) and didn't realize the spill-proof cap was ajar. Mr. Masin spotted a Horton's employee named Vinny who frequents the Box and proceeded to tell him about the Box barista he scalded.

As luck would have it, Dave got so emotional that his arm began to flail while telling the story and he unknowingly spilled his coffee on poor Vinny (burning yet another barista) and on to the floor.

Screaming in agony, Vinny ran to the back to put some hydrogen peroxide and coconut oil on the burn. After the pain and blisters subsided, he would mop the floor. Well, the floor wasn't mopped when John and Tom entered the store. John, not seeing the lake he was about to step in and not realizing that he had the water-resistant sealant on his shoe, sealed his fate.

He slipped and tried to catch himself, but the momentum was too great a force to overcome. He started slipping and sliding like a polar bear on an iceberg. His feet came off the floor like a 747 taking off and, as if in slow motion, his feet flew over his head. Trying to save himself, he turned the fall into a two-and-one-fifth double summersault, triple-lindy dismount, making the famous Wallendas proud. Unfortunately, he missed the landing and fell onto his back.

As Crantzy hit the floor, Gavigan spread his arms out like a baseball umpire, yelling, "Safe, safe, safe!" Don't ask where he got that, who the hell even knew he knew what baseball was.

Then, never one to pass up a free meal or coffee, Mr. Gavigan climbed over the stricken man, walked up to the counter and ordered a large coffee and two doughnuts. The employees and customers were shocked at this utter disregard for human life as the uncaring, unsympathetic, and unembarrassed Gavigan walked over to Crantzy and said, "I don't mean to be an asshole, but I'm a little short this week, can you pick up the tab?" He reached down into Crantzy's wallet pulled out a twenty, paid his bill, and kept the change.

He offered no help to the stricken Crantzy. A little old lady with a walker tried to assist but was told by Gavigan, "Move along, you're cluttering up the accident scene, his lawyer is on the way in his mobile office."

The S.S. Garage Boat

When it comes to the Box, it seems the *Gazette* is never at a loss for stories. I never thought I would write one on MARITIME SALVAGE. And that, my friends, is the plot line of this story.

Our dear friend, Bob Rakoczy, is now officially a snowbird. He spends a great deal of time in Florida in a lovely suburban home located on the inner-coastal, shared with his daughter and son-in-law. Bob came to the Box for the last week of his time in New York and began to share his delightful tale of the Sea.

It started one Saturday evening on his way to the Box when he noticed he misplaced his cigar and trickle charger. He was getting things prepared for his trip to Florida. He wanted to charge the battery to his car but could not find the charger. He wanted to smoke a cigar but could not find that either.

He arrived at the Box flustered and confused. The regulars noticed right away something was amiss. They asked Bob what was wrong. He stated he was having a bad day because he couldn't find his cigar, trickle charger, and now his wallet. He said he was wearing his 180-dollar pair of jeans. This is a shock in itself; that Bob would spend 180 dollars on a pair of jeans when the entire worth of his wardrobe was appraised and rejected by Goodwill.

Bob told of his loss and how he couldn't understand where his wallet was. As always, whenever someone is in trouble, you can always count on your friends at the Box to help. Sweet Lou offered his help and told Bob his wallet is with his cigar and trickle charger. He pondered every word and began to spin his yarn about his new boat.

Apparently sometime during the summer a storm hit the inner coastal and washed a cabin cruiser ashore in the back of Bob's Florida estate. His daughter called him and relayed that he is now the proud owner a washed-ashore cabin cruiser that her handyman Juan Valdez found in the backyard.

Now Juan, mind you, is their new handyman who will fix anything for the right price. According to Bob, the right price is a dollar twenty-five an hour, a Cuban cigar, a Swisher Sweet, and a nice little space in their shed. Shed, you say! Yes, you read that right, shed. It appears Juan had a bit of a spat with his wife and decided the shed was better than living at home. How Bob's daughter found Juan as a handyman is up in the air.

Bob's daughter detests Halloween so much that she had Juan disconnect the doorbell so she wouldn't have to hand out candy. Unfortunately, these two future rocket scientists of NASA never took into account that kids know how to knock on doors. There goes eighty-six cents of labor down the drain. You can't pull a fast one on Bob's daughter or Juan.

While Bob was back in Buffalo for the summer and his daughter back at her palatial estate in Pennsylvania, Juan was left to his own devices. His orders were to put in new windows, hardwood flooring, and other odds and ends for which he would be paid handsomely. I believe somewhere in the neighborhood of eight hundred dollars. However, he was allowed to stay at the Florida home for free.

Knowing his time of sleeping in a room with a real bed and air conditioning was coming to an end because the masters of the estate were returning, Juan began to think. "I need a better place than the shed. I know..." he said to himself in Spanish. A confused look overcame him because Juan realized he had no idea what he said because he doesn't know Spanish and rethought his idea.

THE BOAT! It hit him like a ton of bricks. So he gathered his tools and rope and created a lever system in where he could drag the boat from the backyard to, of all places, the garage. Juan somehow managed to finally get the boat into the garage. How, this reporter doesn't know. It still remains an unsolved mystery.

Bob returned to Florida and discovered he now has to park his brand new BMW hardtop convertible in the blazing sun while Juan resides in the garage on his new houseboat.

There is a bright side to this story. According to the Maritime Salvage Laws, Bob is now the proud owner of a thirty-three-foot cabin cruiser. Also, Bob found his cigar, which Juan was smoking, his trickle charger, which Juan was using to charge the car battery that ran his new boat's air conditioner, and his wallet, which Juan used to finance his new air conditioner and cigar habit.

A side note, the Coast Guard notified Bob the Skipper and Gilligan want their boat back.

Crunch vs. Lunch

An epic battle of wills between two former warriors broke out Friday at the Box. Although this *Gazette* reporter wasn't on hand to witness the carnage, there were enough unreliable, unknown, and mostly anonymous witnesses to relay the story.

The combatants, a former Navy Commander and local cigar peddler known as Captain Crunch, and a former Army Captain and known napkin thief, aka Jimmy the Rug, went ship to tank over the Yankees vs. Jeopardy duel which made the yearly Army-Navy game look like hopscotch.

The Rug fired first with the usual, "put the Yankees game on," which of course is followed by the lack of the word please. Captain Crunch, not to be denied, launched a tomahawk with an, "I'm watching Jeopardy and it's Naval category night."

Intimidation played no part in this battle as the Rug fired a howitzer back, claiming, "I'm the customer, not you, and you put on what the customer wants and just do your job."

Captain Crunch followed with a torpedo across the turret with, "Fuck you, I'm watching Jeopardy! And the Answer is 'Davey Jones' Locker,'" as Crunch also answered the TV.

The Rug pulled out a napkin submarine he made the night before while watching the Yankee game and set it on fire, dropping it into a garbage can.

The outraged Captain Crunch struck back as he grabbed an over-humidified cigar and began to beat the Rug. Unfazed, the

Rug pulled a napkin out and dried himself off and yelled, "Navy Jeopardy is for pussies."

The battle raged for hours and both sides landed shot after shot. The battle got so bad that an anonymous spectator left half a glass of scotch.

Finally, a truce was made. Captain Napkin could watch the Yankee game and Captain Crunch could answer the final Jeopardy question. As the pact was being signed, the anonymous spectator rushed back in and polished off his scotch, saying, "That's worth fighting for."

I'm sure you're all wondering what the final Naval question was. Well, you don't have to wait long, here it is: the answer is John F. Kennedy. The question is "Who was on the ship in the middle of the ocean when Dave was making napalm?

Murder, Not Just for Killing Anymore

We all know that murder is taking someone's life. However, what you may not know, the English language can be murdered in the cruelest of fashions as well.

Box Burns Gazette found someone who is so good, he can destroy one of the greatest lines in a movie and not give it a second thought.

We know this to be true because we have the pleasure of friendship with the serial killer of the entire English language as he shared a cigar and regaled the Box regulars with stories of murder and torture. Shakespeare would be shamed into writing instructional manuals for actors if he possessed this man's command of English.

This man can turn the most common of words into a mystery. His mangling of English has scholars all over the world stumped. If he were alive during World War II, the allies would have used his language as a code. The Axis would have been defeated in three weeks because they would have been driven insane from the intense brainpower needed to figure out what he is saying. The movie *Wind Talkers* would have never been made; it would have been called *JFC Talkers*.

The *Gazette* caught up with long-time Box late-night purveyor Sweet Lou to get some help in translating. Below are just a few of what we were able to learn.

Word Translation:

- Onbelievable: Unbelievable.
- That guy Mario Brando: Marlon Brando.
- He has that AED: A.D.H.D. (Not to be confused with the life-saving equipment).
- DePaul: Nepal (You know, she is from that country near China, DePaul).
- Juicy Juice: Flavor Flav.

This is just a sampling of the mangling of the English language. Movies are no match for this maniacal murderer. The famous line from the Godfather was shot down in cold blood by this ruthless wordsmith.

Instead of, "Leave the gun, take the cannoli," we got, "Leave the cannoli, take the gun." We were left flabbergasted, and his reply was, "You know what I'm talking about, like in that movie with Mario Brando, The Goodfather."

Perhaps the greatest mangling of words happened just other night. All the regulars were at the Box enjoying a cigar when, as usual, John and Tommy G. began to argue and exchange barbs. John ended the argument with, "What the hell is wrong with you? You got that dalexia or something!"

Yes, folks, DALEXIA.

As luck would have it, a car manufacturer was sitting with us and screamed, "Thank you! I've been trying to name my new car model and you've done it for me. It's my new car for dyslexics. All the instruments are written backwards. Right signal is left signal, empty is full, full is empty. The Mirrors are reversed. All I needed was the name, and you've given it to me."

Fortunately, that car never came out and John is currently serving twenty to life in summer school with no chance of libation. I meant liberation, oh crap, how about parole!

Talk-Show Terrors

Now that Oprah is off the air, *Box Burns Gazette* has learned that a new talk show sponsored by the Box will air in June of this year.

It stars Dave Masin and Tom Gavigan. The premise of the show is to turn the conversation into one of two topics. The topics are guns and ponds. Each week a celebrity guest will appear and talk about themselves or projects they are working on and our hosts will turn their topics into guns or ponds.

This *Gazette* reporter was able to get a sneak-peak at the first two episodes. The first guest is Mel Gibson and he will talk about his ex-wife. He chats about how she screwed him and our two hosts turn the conversation into guns and ponds.

Mr. Masin takes over the conversation by yelling, "Mel, Mel, Mel, a good friend of mine back in 1968 named Lyndon Johnson had the same problem with his ex and I advised him to get a nice .44 Magnum, waive it her face a few times, then fire one off by her ear. She'll not only be as deaf as me, she'll straighten right up."

Mr. Gavigan replies, "And by the way, Mel, if you walk her by a pond and accidently trip and hold her head under for a bit, sort of like reverse water boarding, she'll change her tune. Hold on, Mel, you can't do it this week, my pond has a hole in it."

The week after that is astronaut Neil Armstrong to talk about the lunar landing. Mr. Armstrong tells us about when he first stepped out of the Eagle and said, "That's one small step for man, one giant leap for mankind."

But Masin jumps in and says, "NEIL, NEIL, NEIL, wouldn't that have been great if you had a 1942 Garand Sniper Riffle with you? You could have said something like 'The Shot Heard around the World' and fired a round off and that sucker would still be orbiting the moon, which of course might be dangerous because it could have hit other astronauts who landed in later years. I remember my friend Spanky Spankowitz fired a shot at a skunk in our garage, boy did that stink. I guess you could say that was the shot that smelled around the world. Then I had to bury my shirt for three weeks to get the smell out of and it still came out smelling like skunk and dirt."

Mr. Gavigan then steers the conversation back to ponds. "By the way, Neil, were there any ponds on the moon? As I'm sure you are well aware of, I have a pond. Do they have holes in the ponds on the moon? Could you give me a few of those moon rocks, they would look good by my pond, if I could only fix the hole in it. Neil, you know many rocket scientists? Do you think you could send one to my house to solve my pond problem?"

Readers, be sure to tune in for the third episode when the Pope visits their show.

As the Mustache Grows

The Box was graced by the presence of the lovely and very funny wife of an unknown and unnamed home remodeler. She let this *Gazette* reporter in on the secret life of her hammer-heaving hubby while trying set up her daughter with a Syrian nationalist whose main occupation is making dental explosives.

This lovely lady wished to remain anonymous and the only clue to her identity is that she now owns a white Mercedes convertible and has returned home from Florida to change the bed sheets. The *Gazette* got this quote from the bed-sheet-slinging wife, "How the hell can he do million-dollar remodels when he can't figure out how to change the sheets?"

Well, this *Gazette* reporter had the chance to sit down with the homemaker and bookkeeper to the remodeler's empire for an inside look at his hobbies other than drinking Bud.

The most interesting hobby which her hubby partakes is the growing of a white mustache. Much like the great white whale Moby Dick, the great white mustache is a rarity among the human race. The owner of this bushy brush above his lip insists that it is blonde (maybe thirty-five years ago). The *Gazette* has several unreliable witnesses who state with certainty the color blonde left port many years ago and the color bland has docked there permanently, and when he sneezes he looks like a party favor.

Another hobby in which hubby spends his spare time is treasure hunting, No, not under water, but on the beach of southern

Florida. My source informs me she bought him a metal detector for a birthday gift one year and now she can't get him off the beach. The girls that surround him are unbelievable. Unfortunately for him it is to use his mustache as an umbrella to block the UV rays. His wife continued to say that it's not unusual to see him in his Masin Swimwear Collection from morning to night hunting treasure.

That brings another question to the plate. What is the Masin Collection? Well, readers, you asked, and I got it. The Masin Collection is a sleeveless black Raiders shirt complete with spillage on the front, gray swim shorts with matching K-bar knife and Uzi attachments, black knee-high socks, and combats boots.

So what does he do with all the treasure he finds, and what exactly does he find? Good questions. The answer is quite a tale in itself. His kids purchased a little treasure chest where he keeps all his finds.

Here is the unique list:

- Bud Can
- Mustache grooming kit 1965
- One coin
- Key to a Mercedes convertible
- 8-track player (no tractor)
- Dave Masin hunting rifle hidden in the sand by Box regulars (Nice Going, Lloyd Bridges)
- Bottle of thirty-four percent hydrogen peroxide
- Pond replacement kit
- Napkin Dispenser

When asked what he would do with his treasures by his wife, he told her the *Pawn Stars* cast was in town this week and he would bring the treasures to them to see what they would fetch.

Thanks to an anonymous tip from his anonymous wife, the *Gazette* was behind the scenes when Mr. Pauly walked in.

Rick Harrison, star of *Pawn Stars*, watched as Mr. Pauly walked up. He took one look at the mustachioed Dave-Masin-Collection-wearing home remodeler and said "Sir, this is *Pawn Stars*, not Porn Stars."

Mr. Pauly retorted, "Very funny, but I'm here to sell my treasures."

"Let's have a look!" Harrison said. The *Pawn Stars* Star looked at the collection and was stunned that someone actually brought the crap to him. He called over the other cast members and they laughed.

The old man said, "Sir, the dumpsters out back."

Then the camera lights caught something on Mr. Pauly's sleeveless shirt. The expression on the Stars' faces was one of awe, as they could not believe their luck.

Like Moses parting the Red Sea, there it was, spillage from the great Masin Coffee Spill. They were beside themselves and offered an amount of money so great that Mr. Pauly was able to now buy sleeves for his shirt and a razor to shave his 'stache.

Feeling his oats due to the greatest discovery since thirty-four percent hydrogen peroxide, Mr. Pauly told Rick Harrison, "You know, one of my customers said I look like Tom Selleck." Harrison replied "You sure it wasn't Tom Sell It or Tom Shave It?"

Enjoy your treasure, Mr. Pauly. Who knows, next time you may find the tractor that belongs to that 8-track player.

Dancing with Cigars

Two unlikely but yet likely Box clients brought culture to the Box. What normally is used to watch sport, the Box's TV was turned into a cultural extravaganza by this dynamic duo. No, not Batman and Robin, more like Butt Man and Rub Me?

"I thought Liberace was dead," Sweet Lou quipped as in walked the new dancing duo critics. One Mr. Cavanaugh spit out his drink and was fined an under-humidified cigar for spilling on the rug – no, not Jimmy the Rug, the one hiding lake Masin under it – as he caught a glimpse of the two dancing debutants.

Who are these two *Dancing with the Stars* divas? I'm glad you asked. Though they wish to unidentified, the *Gazette* will deny their wishes and reveal them to the readers. The first of the duo came strutting through the door and announced himself with his typical "Hi, men" introduction. Sweet Lou and Mr. Cavanaugh stopped watching the hockey game and looked up to see the pond broker dressed in a powder blue sequence dinner jacket, powder blue pants with a navy stripe on each leg, and Tommy Bahamas loafers, a look that would make Liberace and Elton John jealous.

He announced *Dancing with the Stars* was on tonight. Sweet Lou said, "No fucking way!"

Retorted the Liberace look alike, "Fine, I'll just talk about my pond issues during the game." On came *Dancing with the Stars*!

Who came in next behind little Liberace but the nattily clad ex-Marine dressed in a sleeveless, black, rhinestone Raiders shirt, black cubic-zirconium-studded pants, and glow-in-the-dark combat boots. His entrance was spectacular to say the least as he walked behind the counter and made himself a gallon of coffee. He proceeded to the lounge, looked at the TV, saw that his favorite program was on, tripped over little Liberace's boa, and promptly spilled his coffee, scalding both Charlie and Vinny.

As customers tended to the two scalded victims with hydrogen peroxide and coconut oil, the dynamic duo began commentating on the dancing being done on the show. "Nice pirouette," clapped little Liberace. Nodding his head in agreement, the ex-Marine fashion guru exclaimed, "I would have given them a ten if they had a loaded .44 Magnum in their hands."

And so the night continued. Nice leap, nice catch on the spin, should have danced with a rifle, not an M-16, nice outfits and nice combat boots in that Armed Forces dance. They judged and they judged until mercifully Sweet Lou called it night. "It's 10 p.m. I have to get up at noon, time to go."

Tears rolled from the eyes of the two pretend judges and one was heard yelling, "Fine, if that's the way they want to be, tomorrow it will be all pond all the time!

DoughNUTS

Captain Napkin was fraught with fury as an unnamed nursery magnate rebuffed the precious doughnuts he purchased. Captain Napkin, who many believe still has his first dollar, was visibly shaken as the two doughnuts he purchased from Tim Horton's were not good enough to satisfy the pallet of John Crantzy, aka JFC, and I'm not talking KFC.

The Captain went to Horton's in his 1957 Edsel, using the same tank of gas that came with the car, pulled out his 1945 change purse and aggravated the counter person as he took ten minutes to count out a dollar fifty-seven in pennies, creating a line of cars at the drive-through that stretched down Maple Road to Transit Road. Amherst Police were called in to direct traffic as the Captain dropped a penny on the pavement, delaying everyone another ten minutes.

Finally, the manger had enough and gave him the two Boston cream doughnuts for nothing. Captain Napkin, ever the sly one, exclaimed, "I knew it would work." He got so excited, he put the car in reverse and backed into the car behind him, causing APD to shut down Maple Road.

After leaving the scene of the accident, the Rug drove to the Box and called his new love JFC to tell him his snack was in. When his calls were not returned, he promptly went to the bathroom where he hid out for twenty minutes, creating another line and more angry management. He then went to a chair, which he believes he inherited, and told the unsuspecting Box regular the chair was his and pounded his foot on the ground yelling, "I taught at Canisius and that's my chair!" The regular, who could no longer take it, got up and left his twenty-dollar Dutch master to sit next to a former Marine who was telling all who would listen about the ins and outs of .44 caliber Magnum revolvers.

An ex-non Navy Seal snuck up on the Captain, grabbed the two dastardly doughnuts, and devoured them in thirty seconds, because when you're an ex-non Navy Seal they teach you to eat quick.

As clever as the former non-Seal thought he was, the Rug quickly busted him. Why? The answer is simple. The ex-non Seal had chocolate all over his face, making Larry Mondello of *Leave it to Beaver* fame seem like an amateur. When confronted by the Captain, the pond expert exclaimed, "If you hadn't stolen every napkin in town I would have gotten away with it."

Captain Napkin, irate as he was, cast his anger at JFC as soon as he walked into the Box, exclaiming, "If you had gotten here in time you could have had the doughnuts I wrangled out of Horton's."

The perplexed landscape Barron said, "I didn't want them anyways, I'm in training. I just rode my bike 10 feet and I'm exhausted."

The Box regulars looked at JFC and were puzzled at his remark. One customer asked, "In training for what?"

The nursery magnate replied, "Ohio State needs a quarterback and I'm going back to my old school. I'm back baby, I'm back."

The Captain shook his head and promptly fell asleep in his chair. He woke up later, screaming, "Where is the Yankee game!"

PTSD (Post Toyota Stress Disorder)

The sky was menacing that day, *Gazette* readers. It was a dark, cold, and dreary fall day. An angry pall was cast upon Alternative Brews that night as an unknown member of the wall of drunks met his girlfriend of three weeks out for a few drinks. The boyfriend, as unknown as he is, gave only his initials for this story, J.J. Not accustom to dating a female for more than three hours, he took a chance that fall season only to have things go horribly wrong.

As per his dating ritual, he only takes his date to two places: A.B. and the Box. However, on this occasion he went outside the box and a courtship ensued. He took this unknown medical professional to Dave and Busters and blew his dating budget out of the water. He spent forty dollars on his date that night, thereby exceeding his budget for the next five years, throwing his aura off kilter.

Trying desperately to get his focus back, he met her at Alternative Brews for drinks, not knowing she had the drinking capacity of an ant. The unknown medical professional had four drinks and all bets were off. In walked the Box crew of Milanovich, Cavanaugh, and Sweet Lou for a little socializing. The crew spotted J.J. and said hello. J.J. asked if they would like to meet his friend, the unknown medical professional.

In hindsight, it was a huge mistake. She barely got out the words hello when a wave of nausea hit her worse than a Dave

Masin spill. The queasy queen ran for the bathroom and heaved for all she was worth. Finally, after initially showing no concern for her well-being, J.J. went to her aid. Realizing she would need a ride home, he reluctantly offered, knowing this would put him way behind in the race to have his name on the leaderboard for the wall of drunks.

Much to his dismay, the unknown medical professional told him her car was a standard. J.J. told her he had never driven a standard. Clearly this put him at an impasse because J.J. did not want to spend the night at her place and fall further behind in the race.

J.J. searched high and low for help and he found it in Sweet Lou. He asked Lou if he could drive a standard, and, against his better judgment, Lou said yes and offered his help. Well, the gates of Hell opened up as the queen of alcohol said, "I can't ride with him I don't know him." To which Sweetness replied, "Really! You don't know who you are much less who I am. You can always walk." Reluctantly she relented and handed over her keys.

It only got worse as she pointed to her car. Was it a Taurus? Nope. An SUV? Nope. A Camry? Nope. How about a Toyota Corolla! Give that man a cigar.

"There is no way I can fit in that!" Sweetness exclaimed. Thinking he was out of the deal, he smiled and walked back inside. He was stopped by a horrified scream from J.J. "Oh no! I Called North Bailey Fire Company and they are coming over with the Jaws of Life to get you in. SHIT!"

Here is Sweet Lou's account of the night's events:

After wedging myself in the car, like ten pounds of shit in a five-pound bag, the journey began. I was like a fighter pilot being strapped in for takeoff on an aircraft carrier. Where was my wingman? Goose, are you there? There was no use putting on the seat belt because there was no way in hell if I got into an accident I could possibly be ejected.

I checked the gages and discovered that gas was an option for this woman because she had none! It was below E. I put the heat on and she promptly turned it off yelling, 'I'm hot.' Glad you think so. I turned it back on and told her to shut up. I began to cramp severely because my legs were too long and I was bent at the knees. I now suffer from hyperextended ankles because that was only part of my body I could move.

She began to open her mouth again, I told her, 'if you ain't puking shut it now' and down shifted, throwing her head back into the seat and shutting her up. A Christmas Miracle! As we drove along the I-290, she cried, 'I'm getting sick.' I said, 'you have two choices, you can stick you head out the window or puke in your car.' She again shut up.

Finally we arrived at her house. I extricated myself from the car and immediately began to look for some Gatorade to relieve the cramping. No luck. Behind us J.J. pulled in and he walked her inside in what seemed like thirty minutes, because it was.

He came back out and the ride home began. My new call sign is Maverick because the ride home in J.J.'s car was not much better than the ride there. He of course had no brakes, and so every time we attempted to stop it was like crash landing on a carrier.

When we got to Alternative Brews I called in for a flyby, and of course was denied. We flew by anyway, causing Mr. Masin to spill his drink, causing another flood and closing A.B. until they can get their carpet filthy again.

Sweet Lou was awarded the Box Cross and got an over-humidified cigar for his efforts. J.J. lost his spot on the wall of drunks and promptly dumped the medical professional. Now he spends his time waiting for the handyman to come by.

Olive Garden Mishap

The Olive Garden Italian Restaurant is reviewing its restroom policy following a mishap at its Transit Road location. The mishap involved a Box regular known for stuffing his pockets with hundreds of napkins. He suffered a near fatal fall in the men's room.

One never to use the bathroom at his home, the Rug searches high and low for the eating establishment with the proper facilities. He found that nirvana at the Transit Road Olive Garden.

The Rug began his pre-meal ritual by staking out the bathroom and found it to his liking. He entered the area to cleanse his system of any food residue. This is done to make sure there is plenty of room for the endless salad bar and bread sticks.

The manager was sweating bullets already as he saw the Rug enter his diner. The manager knew his overhead would rise due to the loss of napkins, napkin dispensers, and the numerous heads of lettuce that would be devoured, but never in his wildest imagination did he expect what happened next.

The Rug found his favorite stall, situated his napkins throughout, and began to sit. As he backed in he lost his way to the seat and promptly hit the deck, leaving a mushroom cloud of napkins in the restroom and causing patrons to run for their lives.

The Rug suffered a massive scratch to his left arm and a crushed napkin dispenser. He staggered out of the restroom like a man who just listened to three hours of Dave Masin Marine escapades. The manager, shocked at what he saw, immediately got the injured Rug a chair. All the Rug could utter is, "PUT THE YANKEE GAME ON."

The Rug screamed, "Get me a bandage, tourniquet, and a phone, I'm injured worse than Jeter and I'm calling the Lexus Lawyer!" The manager lowered his head and complied and got Captain Napkin a bandage for the scratch.

The Rug gave a wink to no one in particular as visions of free meals danced through his rug. In walked the Lexus Lawyer, who got there quickly, due the fact he was at a nearby drive-through working with a client. Immediately he called for an ambulance and had the Rug rushed to another eating establishment. The Lexus Lawyer gave the manager his license plate number and said "I'll be in touch, and by the way, do you have a drive-through? My clients love this place."

The Olive Garden offered Jimmy two free meals and $50,000 for a settlement. The Rug was so overwhelmed that he forgot to confer with his Lawyer and just took the free meals. When the Lexus Lawyer heard this he crashed into a drive-through and is now being sued himself.

The makers of the bomb sights for the B-2 Stealth Bombers called Jimmy and offered him a bomb sight that will track the path to the toilet seat and guide him in so this will never happen again. The Rug of course accepted on one condition, that they throw in a few free meals.

History's Mysteries

When was the last time anyone actually used the information they learned in history class? That time finally has finally come.

It was a dark, muggy Sunday, Memorial Day eve evening, the city restless, no sports on, and the Box was open for business because no one had anything better to do.

A group of regulars crowed around the television because there aren't that many chairs to sit in. The after-hours purveyor circled the stations like the Indians circled Custer and found nothing but war movies on AMC. Sweet Lou was badgered by suggestions from the crowd.

Taunts of *Dancing with the Stars,* the Gun Channel, Marine movie marathon with commentary from former Marine Corporal David Masin and Gunnery Sergeant R. Lee Ermy, the Cooking Channel from Mr. Milanovich, and Bob Villa from one Mr. Pauly. Is Villa even still alive?

Finally the movie Midway was chosen. The crowd settled in. Mr. Cavanaugh had his scotch, Mr. Pauly his case of Bud, the Lexus Lawyer had his normal double Scotch and keys in hand waiting for the next client to pick up, Mr. "I don't want anything" Milanovich refused all drink requests and was given a drink anyway, the pond and garden expert had his Sambuca and a bottle of thirty-four percent hydrogen peroxide, Mr. Masin spilled his drink, Mr. Crantzy a Snickers Bar for the tooth, and Sweet Lou had pen and paper to document any mishaps.

Sweetness was not disappointed and had his first note as the title Midway appeared on the screen two seconds into the movie. The pond master chimed in with, "Who won this battle?"

Stunned silence erupted except for the haunting sound of, "Tom, Tom, Tom, did you know that back on December 7th, 1941, the United States was attacked by the Japanese and thirty years to the day, I sold the pilot of the first Jap Zero to bomb Pearl Harbor a 1964 Pontiac GTO?"

Here we go! There was still two hours and fifty-eight seconds of the movie left and so the night continued.

The longer the movie ran, the more questions and stories followed. "Who was Admiral Halsey and why is he in the hospital?" Came the question from the non-famous historian Tom Gavigan. Sweet Lou answered again with, "The Admiral was supposed to take over the carrier Yorktown when he came down with a contagious rash."

Then, as if on cue, "Tom, Tom, Tom, did you know that while I was making napalm in 1961, President Kennedy waived to Spanky Spankowitz and me from a carrier in the Atlantic Ocean, and do you know who was captain? It was Admiral Halsey's son."

The night continued on and so did the drinking. Finally the movie ended, but not the questions nor the stories. To reduce the questions, a World War II flashcard was made by Sweet Lou to aid the history-challenged pond maker. Here it is:

Battle	USA	Japan	Germany	Russia
Pearl Harbor		X		
Midway	X			
Stalingrad				X
Battle of the Bulge	X			
Anzio	X			
Iwo Jima	X			
Poland/France			X	

So get some popcorn, drinks, and settle in for the Box's new after-hours event, WAR MOVIE NIGHT, with guest hosts Dave and Tom.

50 Minus 49 First Dates

Readers may be wondering if these stories go beyond the men who just hang at the Box, and the short answer is yes. Box misjudgments extend to all generations, and *Box Burns Gazette* uncovered one such generational prodigy, one Phillipo Milanovich Jr (PMJ). Here is his tale of woe as discovered by this reporter.

Most if not all of us remember Christmas Break from school. It was a time when we looked forward to relaxing, forgetting about what we learned, and enjoying the holidays with family and friends.

However, that all changed when this reporter was told PMJ had brought his entire school locker home with him on Christmas vacation to study for a midterm five weeks from now. His father was so disturbed by this this and the fact that he had to borrow Mr. Pauly's Ford 750 to haul the books home that he had PMJ checked for concussion symptoms.

Then another shocking revelation came to the surface when PMJ told Box regulars on his first day of Christmas vacation he returned to his grammar school to visit and hang with his former teachers and promptly got escorted from the building. This kid can't get enough of school buildings. He is in them so much that his high school Principal gave him a perfect attendance award for being in school when it was not in session.

Just when you thought this kid, who has plenty of book smarts but the common sense of a shell-shocked napalm maker, couldn't do anything else, he delivered the tale of his very first date.

So while I have your attention let me take back to the moment he asked his date out to the date itself.

We take you back to the halls of St. Joseph's High School where we see PMJ talking to his friend, Mitchell, about asking Sylvia Spankowitz from Sacred Heart to the high school dance. Spankowitz, the daughter of Spanky and niece of Sparky Spankowitz, has been a heartthrob to PMJ for years.

PMJ and Mitchell came up with a plan for PMJ to ask her out on a date. Here is that conversation.

PMJ: Duh, Mitch, you know that Sylvia Spankowitz.

Mitch: Duh, huh yeah.

PMJ: Duh, well I'm, uh huh, going to ask her to the school dance.

Mitch: Really! Wow, man, you have some balls, duh. I mean testicles. Uh huh, duh, you know last time you asked her out she said she was busy coloring between the lines. Duh.

PMJ: Well, Mitch—

Mitch: It's MITCHELL.

PMJ: Well, Mitch, as I was saying, I have this foolproof plan. I ask her to go as a friend. There is no way she can say no.

Mitch: It's Mitchell, and that is the best idea I have ever heard of. Maybe I should go to school on Saturdays and Sundays, too. Wouldn't that be cool, you and I sitting here all by ourselves studying.

PMJ: That is pretty much what we do Monday through Friday.

Mitch: Oh yeah, I forgot, Duh!

The night of the date, PMJ began to don his wardrobe. First he put on his white socks and underwear, complete with a belt to prevent the seniors giving him a wedgie. Next the pants, hemmed high enough to show off his white socks with St. Joes embroidered on them.

Then the long-sleeve shirt with the sleeves ending at his elbows, and a rainbow-colored bow tie. He got a rake to comb his hair and greased it back. He then got into his father's car so he and dad could pick up Sylvia for the big date.

Milanovich asked, "Are you ready for your date?"

PMJ responded, "As ready as I'll ever be. I took the advice of the Terrorist, Mr. Gavigan, and Mr. Masin. The Terrorist told me how to pick up girls and have a relationship. You know, Dad, I'm not so sure I should take his advice on women. I was in pre-school longer than he was married."

"Now you are getting it, son. By the way, why aren't you wearing the suit your mother and I bought you?"

"Well, Dad, Mr. Masin gave me the cut-off combat boots with the steel bottoms and told me to wear them because you never know when a kid is going to throw an M-80 on the dance floor and that I could possibly step on it and blow a toe off. Then he gave me the camouflage suit jacket so that I would blend in with the auditorium walls in case the date went bad. Mr. Masin said always be prepared and told me the suit coat and boots were from the Masin Collection."

"Oh, God," replied the senior Milanovich. "Son, why are the pants so short?

"Mr. Gavigan gave me his new Park Club pants and said women loved him in them." The senior Milanovich replied, "That guy, never taller than a leprechaun." Oh well, too late now.

PMJ arrived at Sylvia's house to pick her up. On the porch were Spanky and his daughter waiting for PMJ to arrive. Mr. Milanovich noticed an orange substance on Spanky's hands and asked him what that was. Spanky looked at his hands and said, "Oh this! I was just making orange Jell-O with my good friend Dave and he spilled it on my kitchen floor, burning a hole clear to the basement. We were just cleaning it up. You should see Dave; his clothes are burnt to a crisp. I told him not to stir it too fast."

Sylvia walked to the car and saw PMJ dressed in the Masin Collection and immediately put on sunglasses and pulled out a walking cane. This is going to be a long night. Little did she know! When PMJ got out of the car he reached for his book bag. Mr. Milanovich grabbed the bag and said, "No way! Your clothing choice is enough to make me tell you that you were adopted, now this? No!"

"Dad, I have a midterm!"

The elder Milanovich screamed, "Your GPA is 6.5, you don't need to do this! Skip a class, miss a question, or take a sick day, for God's sake, but not this. Where did I go wrong?"

PMJ grabbed the bag and his date and ran to the auditorium. The dance began and PMJ sat with his date and book bag strapped to his back. He asked Sylvia if she'd like a drink. She said yes just so he would leave.

Unfortunately for her, the punch bowl was within arm's length of where PMJ was sitting. He never left her side. You see, Box fans, being a genius, PMJ calculated where he would have to sit so he didn't have to leave here side. He used Pauly Mathematics, where all answers come out to be a million.

Sylvia asked PMJ, "Why do you have your book bag?"

PMJ responded, "To study for my midterms between dances. She screamed and put on another pair of sunglasses.

Then the music started and the first song was "Cheap Sun Glasses" by ZZ top. PMJ looked at Sylvia's glasses and asked her to dance. This had disaster written all over it.

PMJ got up with book bag strapped to his back and they began to dance. There were tears coming from Sylvia's eyes because

PMJ stepped on her feet with his steel-bottom soles. The music was too loud for anyone to hear her scream. However, I wish I could say it ended there. As the song went on and Sylvia limped through the dance, PMJ decided to do a spin. OH THE HUMAN-ITY! As he spun he forgot about the book bag strapped to his back and it nailed poor Sylvia Spankowitz. The girl flew across the auditorium like she was hit by a tornado, hitting the opposite wall, striking her head, and knocking out fourteen students as she flew through the air. It was like someone yelled "fire!" at a crowded movie theatre. Bodies everywhere. It took twelve ambulances to clean the carnage.

The kids were treated and released. Sylvia was in a coma and treated for two broken feet. The doctors told her father that she was so traumatized and crippled that she may never dance again, ending her dream of becoming a dancer on *Dancing with the Stars.* As PMJ stood in shocked silence, Mitchell, who also had a book bag strapped to him, tapped PMJ on the shoulder and said, "Maybe we should have stayed home and played Halo with your mom." They both shook their heads in agreement.

The next day PMJ visited Sylvia in the hospital. He had brought her flowers in a sippy cup. As he moved closer to the bed he saw that she was sleeping, but he did not see the cord to the IV. He tripped, spilling water all over her, and ripped out her IV. Thank God she was unconscious. The water did wake her from her coma and thankfully she didn't remember a thing.

PMJ was not allowed to dress up for any special occasions without the help of his parents where there were human beings involved, and the assault with a dangerous weapon charge was dropped by Mr. Spankowitz and Sylvia, because she was still in a fog and being treated for a concussion by the Cleveland Browns medical staff.

The Masin Collection was discontinued for all high school dances, Mr. Gavigan was given a restraining order, ordering him not to lend his pants to anyone taller than five feet, and the Terrorist was deported for giving away terrorist dating advice.

The Case of the Missing Marines

It was June 16, a comfortable spring evening. Sweet Lou was working the night watch at the Box. All the regulars were in, Mr. Cavanaugh, Milanovich, Rooster, the pond maker, Mr. Pauly, Mr. Crantzy, the Lexus Lawyer, his client the Rug, and Mr. Masin. Three Marines also happened to be at the Box that night.

They were watching the seventh and final game of the Stanley Cup. All the chairs were taken when the three Marines came in and decided to sit at the table and discuss boot camp with the newest Marine. They bought their cigars and began their discussions. The Box's Marine historian, former Lance Corporal Masin, joined them. A sigh of relief came over the crowd, as the hockey game was free of any Marine topics. It turned out to be an uneventful night as the Bruins claimed the Cup.

June 17 was a busy evening at the Box. Sweet Lou was still working the night watch selling cigars. Two men with high and tight haircuts walked in and browsed around. They breezed by the cigars and studied the crowd, never saying hello to anyone. They pulled out their badges, NCIS.

The following is what took place:

Agent Thursday: I'm Thursday, this is Cannon. We're investigators.
Sweet Lou: How can I help you?
They pulled out three photos.

Agent Thursday: Have you ever seen these three Marines?

Sweet Lou: Yes.

Agent Cannon: Where?

Sweet Lou: Here.

Agent Thursday: Here where?

Sweet Lou: Sitting at that table.

Agent Thursday: Who else was with them?

Sweet Lou: Where?

Agent Cannon: Here.

Sweet Lou: Another Marine.

Agent Thursday: Who?

Sweet Lou: A former Corporal.

Agent Thursday: What's his name?

Sweet Lou: Whose name?

Agent Cannon: His name! What's his name?

Sweet Lou: The Corporal?

NCIS Agents: Yes, for Christ's sake!

Sweet Lou: Well why didn't you say so? It was Masin, he's over there.

Agent Thursday: Where?

Sweet Lou: There!

Agent Cannon: Where is there?

Sweet Lou: Who are you guys, Abbott and Costello! He is over *there*!

Sweet Lou finally pointed him out, and Thursday and Cannon pulled Mr. Masin aside to talk.

Agent Cannon: Ok, Marine, where are they?

Masin: Who?

Agent Cannon: The three Marines you spoke to yesterday.

Masin: Where?

Agent Cannon: Here!

Masin: Here where?

Cannon was getting upset as another Abbott and Costello routine was beginning. Thursday stepped in to relieve his partner.

Agent Thursday: Where are they?

Masin: Who?

Agent Thursday: The Marines!

Masin: Who?

Agent Thursday: The three marines you spoke to yesterday.

Masin: Where?

Agent Thursday: Here!

Masin: Oh! Well back in 1962 I was talking to three Marines while fixing a tank and lost my hearing...or did they lose *their* hearing?

Agent Thursday: Who?

Masin: The three Marines!

Agent Thursday: Which Marines!

Masin: Which three Marines? The ones here last night, what about them?

Agent Thursday: They are missing!

Masin: Missing!

Agent Thursday: Yes, missing! What do you know about them?

Masin: Who?

Agent Thursday: THE MARINES!

It was at this point that Cannon reentered the fray.

Agent Cannon: Ok, wise guy, listen and listen good. There are three missing Marines and they trained hard and long. You know who paid for that training? That's right, you and I, with our hard-earned tax dollars. And now they are missing. Why? I don't know, but Uncle Sam pays me to find out why.

Masin: Why what?

Agent Cannon: Why they are missing.

Masin: Well I don't know why. That's your job, not mine.

Clearly frustrated by the lack of progress, Thursday and Cannon turned again to Sweet Lou.

Agent Thursday: Can you help?

Sweet Lou: The three Marines had enough of the Corporal's stories and just wanted to go back to Iraq where it was peaceful.

NCIS Agents: Oh! We can't blame them, we were ready to go there ourselves if this went on any longer.

The three Marines did indeed return to Iraq ready to fight and are also being treated for Post Traumatic Masin Story Syndrome (PTMSS). Thursday and Cannon promptly retired from NCIS.

Mr. Masin still tells his stories to a new crop of Marines and the list of volunteers to go back overseas is climbing. Sweet Lou still works the night watch.

Cross-Country Encounters of another Kind

Just when you thought you have heard it all at the Box, another surprise pops up.

While enjoying a meal at the home of nursery owner John Crantzy, Jimmy the Rug, overcome with the intoxicating fullness of a twenty-five-course Milanovich meal that left the nursery magnate over the limit on his credit card, admitted to a startling revelation after going to the Box for an after-dinner cigar.

Jimmy informed a stunned group of Box regulars that he was an athlete at Amherst High School back in the early twentieth century. Jimmy, known for his passion of napkin gathering, informed the group that he had tried out for football but did not make the team. The *Gazette* did some research and found out why. A long exhaustive search ensued to find a former teammate that was alive and not residing in a nursing home.

The former teammate, who wishes to remain anonymous, whose name is Spanky "Napalm" Spankowitz, tells this tale.

Jimmy was well liked by all the guys on the team because whenever we got cut he always had a napkin on hand to bandage us up. It was uncanny. I believe his helmet was made of napkins.

Jimmy tried out at QB but was quickly asked to try something else because when he tried to call a play he fell asleep during the call and would yell 'put the Yankees game on.' He tried several other positions to no avail. The last straw was during a scrimmage. We were scrimmaging Holy Angels. Yeah, it was an all-girl school, but they had a lot of tough-looking girls who went there. Well, we got a penalty. The ref threw the yellow knotted-up flag and Jimmy came strolling off the bench, picked up the flag and told the ref, 'Now I have a classy dinner napkin.' The ref gave us a 15-yard penalty that cost us the game and Jimmy his spot on the team.

Jimmy did find a sport that he was a match for: Cross-country. It took Jimmy quite a while to get used to the sport. He finally learned that every time you ran past a food joint that you did not have to stop in for a bite to eat. Jimmy got lost a lot running cross-country so the coach put a trail of napkins down so he could find the finish line.

Jimmy took to the sport and had almost made it through the season when disaster struck. Jimmy was leading the race coming down the home stretch, the finish was a mere five feet away, when he tripped over a knotted-up yellow dinner napkin lying on the gravel track. Jimmy had visions of Teds Hot Dogs dancing in his head and did not see the napkin lying in wait. He started to fall, hitting the gravel track at such a slow rate of speed that it looked like slow motion, and it would have been, except slow motion hadn't been invented yet. Out came the hands and down came the knees, skidding on the gravel and scraping every inch of his hands and knees. When Jimmy stopped his momentum six inches later, he looked at his wounded hands and knees and promptly fainted at the sight of the blood and scratches.

Jimmy awoke yelling, "DiMaggio, Berra, and Stengel!" He heard an angel voice saying, "You'll be ok, Jimmy, it's just a cut." Jimmy looked at her and realized it was a cheerleader carrying him back to the bench. It was love at first napkin.

Unfortunately the love story ended three days later when she gave Jimmy and ultimatum. It was the napkins or her. Guess which one he picked?

My Kingdom for my Keys

Where oh where did a huge set of keys go? That was the question. After a hard day's work, Sweet Lou decided that a cigar was in order. As he entered the store, he ran into a customer in distress. Sweet Lou, always customer conscious, offered his help to the new cigar enthusiast. Sweetness set his keys down on the counter, helped the customer, and went to the lounge.

After ordering dinner Sweet Lou checked on his keys and discovered they were not in his pockets. The search of the century ensued. The FBI didn't look for Lindbergh's baby this hard. Sweet Lou began a cursory search of the Box, checking the lounge and then the front of the store. No luck. The second phase of the search took place as the search area widened to the Bocce Club Pizzeria. No luck.

A search party was now formed. The group included Jimmy D., Jimmy the Rug, Rooster, the Mad Syrian, and John Crantzy. The party scoured the Box from front to back, side to side. Again, no luck. Sweet Lou asked if anyone picked up his keys; everyone checked, no keys.

The Rug threw out this gem, "check your pockets."

Sweet Lou responded, "Jimmy, I did already."

Next the search and rescue team asked Crantzy to check his chair. Crantzy yelled "they're not here, I checked." Crantzy reluctantly got up, got his workout for the week in, found nothing, and promptly responded, "I told you they were not here."

Jimmy again offered his sage advice, "Check your pockets!"

Sweet Lou yelled at him again. "Jimmy, I did!"

Sweetness pondered the situation longer and retraced his steps. Since there weren't that many steps it was easy. No luck. A familiar voice erupted from the back, "Check your pockets!"

Sweet Lou's patience was fraying. Panic began to set in as calls were made to the regulars sitting next to Lou. A call to the Park Club was made. "Tom, did you pick up my keys by mistake?" No luck. "Can you ask Ray?" No luck.

"Check Your Pockets!" came from the back.

"How many fucking pockets do you think I have, Jimmy?" yelled Lou. "John, can you check your chair again?"

"What the fuck!" yelled Crantzy, "how much exercise can I do in one day!"

No luck once again. An idea struck Lou to go to the Park Club and check Ray's Car. Mr. Milanovich offered a ride to Sweet Lou and he accepted.

Sweet Lou checked Ray's car, no luck. Lou, after checking Ray's car, heard a faint irritating voice "Check your pockets!" Sweet Lou looked into the sky and yelled, "Why Me!" He entered the Park Club and found Tom and Ray drinking with the boys. Ray again checked his pockets, no luck. They asked Lou and Mr. Milanovich to join them for a drink. Sweet Lou wasn't in the mood and Mr. Milanovich always refuses. Once he refused water as he was dying from thirst in the Sahara Desert.

Ray graciously offered his Toyota Avalon for Sweet Lou to use so he could get his spare keys in Hamburg. Could he live any further away?

As a flashback of another Toyota episode played in his mind, he squeezed in and headed for home.

Unbeknownst to Lou, a prayer group was formed at the Box led by Pastor Rooster and Jimmy the Altar Boy. They prayed for the lost keys to be found. Jimmy prayed for Sweet Lou to check his pockets. Sweet Lou began his trek, cursing all the way, thinking what a way to make the *Box Burns Gazette*. Maybe no one will mention it. Not Likely! As Sweet Lou hit Millersport and Maple a call came. It was Jimmy D. stating his father Steve found the keys. "Where?" Sweet Lou asked. The keys were in the lighter bin. "How could that be, I checked there," he said out loud to no one in particular.

Sweet Lou arrived back at the Box to retrieve his keys, thanked everyone for their help and wound up in the *Box Burns Gazette*.

The Rug offered this advice to Sweet Lou: "You should really keep your keys in your POCKETS!

Vow of Silence Broken

Omerta, the word for silence among organized-crime figures, was cast aside as a Box regular broke his two-day code of silence. The unnamed former Marine vowed to be silent about his beloved Marines due to the verbal beating he has taken from non-Marine Box regulars, as well as the sudden fame he has achieved from this reporter about his exploits that he constantly talks about.

Joe Thursday, a special contributor to the *Box Burns Gazette* from time to time and a former NCIS agent, conducted an interview with this former marine.

Joe: Hello, Marine.

Marine: Hello, Joe, did I ever tell you about the time President Kennedy waved to me?

Joe: No, I never heard that one.

Marine: Well, Joe, let me tell you, it was back in 1961...

Joe: It's ok, Marine, we only have twenty minutes. May I call you by your first name?

Marine: No you may not! My friend Frank Tully was the only who called me by first name and he played football for Holy Cross, did you know that, Joe?

Joe: No I did not, and what does that have to do with what I call you?

Marine: It doesn't, however, in 1965 when I bought my first car, a 1964 GTO, many people called it a goat!

Joe: Let's get on track, Marine, why the vow of silence?

Marine: Well, Joe, like my napalm partner, Spanky Spankowitz, used to say back in the sixties: make napalm not love, and burn the bastards out of their homes!

Joe: That makes no sense!

Marine: If you were in the Marines you would understand it.

Joe: I was and I don't! Are you on crack?

Marine: Be careful, Joe, I do 2,000 crunches a week and I could bore you death in five minutes.

Joe: Ok, ok, Marine, you don't have to tell me another story. Why the vow?

Marine: As I was saying, every time I began to tell Marine stories weird things would take place.

Joe: Like what?

Marine: It is hard to explain. Back in '62 when I was washing tanks with Spanky – you see, Spanky and I were a pair...

Joe: Hey, Sweet Lou, is *Pawn Stars* or *True Grit* on?

Marine: Joe, Joe, Joe, can you hear me?

Joe: What?

Marine: See what happens? Now I'll be in that damn newsletter. Thanks for nothing!

Joe: What?

Marine: Weren't you listening?

Joe: What?

Marine: You missed my whole story on the Vow of Silence.

Joe: I did? Thank God!

And so it went, one story after another. Joe's interest faded and after five minutes he fell asleep and forgot about the interview. The Marine took another vow and now pulls his car in forward instead of backwards.

The Marine, who wishes to remain nameless, vowed again never to talk about his beloved Marines and now spends a good portion of his days trying to eradicate the ash beetle by bringing samples of his tree to the Box for JFC to examine. Crantzy predicts that if he continues to bring in samples of his tree he will have none left within five days. Which will last longer: the vow of silence or the ash trees?

Take me Out of the Ball Game

The cry of "put the Yankees on" is nothing compared to what Buffalo's biggest nursery magnate experienced. The magnate, known as J.F. Crantzy, decided it would be a great idea to take Yankee fan extraordinaire Jimmy the Rug to his son's baseball game.

This idea had disaster written all over from the get go. Kids' ball games are mainly played at night, and guess what team plays at night as well? That's right, the world's most annoying team, the Yankees.

As the Rug attempted to get into John's truck, a problem arose. Jimmy could not get in because the truck was too high off the ground. Jimmy, being the athlete he was, could not lift his leg more than an inch off the ground and was stopped in his tracks.

So after studying the problem, it was determined by the Rug there were two solutions to the problem: A high lift should be called in to lift Jimmy into the truck, or John could drive home and get his Escalade. Neither solution was acceptable to JFC, so he just picked up Jimmy by the scruff of his neck, because that's where he wears his pants, and threw him into the truck. Problem solved, strike one.

The Rug, never one to miss an opportunity to have a full course meal, decided it was time to eat. JFC was beside himself, already fashionably late, as they missed the first three innings of a six-inning game and Jimmy wants food. Jimmy asked JFC where the concession stand was and JFC pointed like Babe Ruth pointing to the outfield against the loveable Cubs. Jimmy got in line and JFC went to watch his son play.

Twenty minutes went by and no sign of the Rug. JFC wondered if he could be in the bathroom. Possibly, but probably not, he hasn't eaten in the last twenty minutes. JFC found Jimmy in line and about to order. All of a sudden JFC heard Jimmy screaming. What was this about? Jimmy had tried to order six hot dogs and was refused. Why? Well, as his luck would have it, Jimmy was in the ice cream line. No hot dogs for you! Jimmy yelled, "I'm going to get an ice cream after I eat these hot dogs." The concession lady yelled, "No, you're in the wrong line, and put those napkins back!" Strike two, another inning missed. Only two innings left.

Jimmy finally got to his seat and was surrounded by several women. He turns to JFC and said that woman is hot and started to talk to her. The Rug engaged her in a conversation for ten minutes and she asked if he would like to meet her eighty-six-year-old mother. Jimmy retorted, "I want you!" Foul ball, still strike two.

Jimmy saw another woman walk down the aisle and said to JFC she is really cute. JFC looked at Jimmy like he had six hot dogs stuck in his mouth (at one point he did but not now) and yelled, "That's my sister!" Foul tip, still strike two.

Another woman slips by and sat next to JFC, and Jimmy, still on the hunt with a full stomach, said to JFC, "that woman looks good from behind and she moves pretty good, too." JFC, looking like a sunstroke victim, stood up and yelled, "That's my Mother!" Strike three, game over.

The good news is JFC's son won the game and advanced to the championship game. The bad news is JFC is banned from the championship game for yelling, and the Rug is banned from the game as well for stealing all their napkins.

American Pickers Visit Pauly Pavilion

Jim Pauly, owner of the world famous Pauly Pavilion, has mistakenly told this reporter that the stars of History Chanel's *Americans Pickers* visited him last week.

When the Pickers arrived, the world's most vicious goose immediately attacked them. The Pickers, Mike and Frank, were trapped inside their van until groundskeeper Jesse came out to save the day. Jesse explained to them he would came out sooner, but he couldn't find his teeth he lost the night before at the Saturday Night Square Dance. Jesse went on to say that his date flung him across the room and his teeth came flying out and got stuck in the wood. It took the local Syrian dentist three hours to extract them.

As the Pickers finally got out of the truck, Mr. Pauly, the owner of this ponderosa, pulled into the drive way and greeted the boys.

Frank looked at Mike and said, "We did it again, we found another celebrity, one Mr. John Holmes of XXX fame."

Mr. Pauly held up his hands and told the boys, "Pump the breaks, it's only me, Jim Pauly, your common garden variety home improvement, Mercedes, and relationship expert, whose motto is 'Every once in a while you got to fuck things up.'"

The Pickers were dumbfounded as they stared at Mr. Pauly's Mustache. Mike told Frank, "I've got to break the ice or we will never get a hold of one those twelve Allis Chalmers tractors. I'm

going to offer him five dollars to sell that mustache; we have several underage clients who would pay twenty for that 'stache to
look older to buy beer." Frank responded, "Good point, Mike!"

Mr. Pauly stroked his mustache and pondered the offer and
said no sale. "I hate to contribute to ruination of America. However, boys, I do have a Springfield rifle brought down here to the
Pavilion by an unknown, not-so-good expert named..."

Mike interrupted Jim, "Hold on there, Mr. Pauly, I believe we
met this guy; he tried to sell us Napalm he made down at the
corner gas station. He told us President Kennedy watched him
and his friend make it from the middle of the Atlantic Ocean. We
passed on that item, then of all things he spilled a little on
Frank's shoe. Poor Frank was frantic and kicked off the Napalm
into a gas pump and blew the frigging gas station to kingdom
come. We had to file Police reports out all night, that's why we
were late."

"Well, boys, that is one in the same. You see, he came down
here one weekend and gave his gun to an eight-year-old to shoot.
Can you believe that, why not hand the kid a bazooka and let him
blow his brains out? Anyway, I digress. As I was saying, I took
the gun from the eight-year-old, gave it back to the so called expert, and said you shoot it. Well, if luck didn't have it, he fired the
gun and nothing happened. The expert began to look down the
barrel to find the problem; you might as well sit in the bathtub
and throw in a radio if you want to kill yourself. The gun didn't
fire because the last time it had been cleaned George Washington
was a Captain, and not to mention the expert put so much gun-
powder in the chamber that he could have set off a howitzer."

Frank looked at Mike and said he had to have the gun. "Ok,
Mr. Pauly, I'll give you five bucks for the gun and a thousand
bucks for the story." Pauly yelled "Sold!"

The boys made their move for the tractors, there were twelve
of them. They heard Mr. Pauly yell, "Damn! I could have sworn I

only had eight." Then the sweat began to pour down Pauly's brow. "If my wife finds out I have twelve of these things she'll want a Bentley. Well, boys, it's your lucky day, you can have any three of these lovely tractors for free, just get them out of here in the next fifteen minutes or I'm in the hole $300,000 for a new Bentley."

Mike said it was a deal and shook the relieved Mr. Pauly's hand. "Damn, I have to learn to use my toes when I count," exclaimed a distraught but relieved Mr. Pauly.

Until next time, when another Box customer does something totally stupid.

Bickering Baggers

The Park Club has announced today that they are conducting an internal investigation concerning allegations and manifestations of alleged disturbing and bickering behavior on the part of a long-time club member and soon-to-be former teammate.

The two parties involved shall remain anonymous, but if you must know and since I am no reporter, thus have no oath, they will not. Here is the *Box Burns Gazette's* rendition done to the theme of *Gilligan's Island*.

Gavigan's Island

Just sit right back and you will hear a tale,
A tale of fateful golf trip,
That started from the Park Club Course,
Aboard a tiny cart.

The mate was a tiny golfing man,
The partner couldn't count.
Four golfers set out that day,
For a four hour round, a four hour round.

The temperature starting getting hot,
The tiny cart was cramped,
If not for the counting of the bickering two,

The tournament would be lost, the tournament would be lost.

The cart set ground on the fringe that day, of an uncharted sand
trap.
With Gavigan, the Landscaper too,
The Cigar Store owner and his lighter,
Mr. Cavanaugh and the rest,
Here on Gavigan's Course.

Tom Gavigan, and the Landscaper too,
Will do their very best,
To make sure their scores are unbeatable,
In this Park Club Contest.

Wrong clubs, bad shots, so many Mulligans,
Not a single ounce of golf etiquette,
Like Dangerfield in Caddy Shack.
As messed up as it gets, as messed up as it gets.

So join us here each day, my friends,
Your sure do get a smile.
From two bickering pals who claim to be friends,
Here on Gavigan's Course.

Unfortunately, the investigation turned up nothing but ag-
gravation. This lead to a suspension from the club for three
months for all parties involved.

Roughing it with Jim "Bear Grilles" Pauly

Readers, did you know that one of our very own could spin a yarn about the rough conditions of hunting Elk in Colorado? I bet you thought I was talking about Dave Masin, but you would be wrong on all counts. This tale came from that home improvement magnate, proud owner of the porn mustache and white convertible Mercedes, the one and only Jim Pauly.

It was a crisp autumn Monday evening at the Box. The regulars were gathered around the television waiting for Hank Williams to compare Obama to Hitler and get himself thrown off Monday Night Football. I'll miss "Are you ready for some football, a Monday night party." There was a packed house at the Box as everyone began to get comfortable for the game. The Rug was screaming to put the game on and only thirty minutes remained before kickoff. As usual, he was asleep before the game started and was dreaming of the napkins that made up his bed.

The Terrorist was telling everyone about his new Fiat 300 and how he beat a skateboarder in the quarter mile once the 350 snail-power fiat engine kicked in. It does zero to sixty in three and a half days. Gavigan was trying to recruit more people for his Florida trip just in case the Terrorist blew himself up by mistake, thus being forced to drive to Florida by himself, and the way he swerves he might be in Kansas way before Florida.

The crowd was waiting for Hank when Mr. Pauly began to tell us of the difficulties he would encounter while roughing it in

Colorado. First, he had to drive 1,500 miles in his brand spanking new (again, no reference to Masin) Ford F-750. This truck is so big that Ford had to double the 350 and add fifty. It has a refrigerator to hold seven cases of Bud just for the trip down, sleeps seven comfortably, has power inverters to hook up every electrical device known to mankind, and what made this so sweet is that he could connect his c-pap machine and drive while he was sleeping.

Gavigan chimed in, "What's so special about that, I drive like that daily." The only thing missing from that truck was a KC-10 tanker to fill it up while driving.

After that long arduous drive he would have to set up camp. We all figured he'd sleep in a tent on the ground; no heat, no running water, no bathroom, and no stove to cook.

Were we wrong to assume this was roughing it? Little did we know that roughing it to Mr. Pauly was a five-star hotel. Here is just a day in the life of the great White Hunting 'Stache.

He got out to the great state of Colorado and pulled up to the ranch he would be hunting at and was met by a valet and bell hop. The bellhop unloaded his gear and brought it up to his suite while the valet washed and hand-waxed his truck and got rid of all evidence of any cigar residue or smell. This car smelled so good that it made the women of the anti-smoking league want to ride in it.

Mr. Pauly was met by a Ricardo Montalban look-alike named Tex and the midget from the *Austin Powers* movie, Mini Tex.

Tex said, "Welcome to Fantasy Hunt Camp, Mr. Pauly, your suite is right up the stairs. We will have someone carry you up as to not tire you out so you'll be ready for lunch."

As he entered the suite, Mini Tex was there with a robe and a cigar. "Your Jacuzzi is ready, Mr. Pauly."

Mr. Pauly exclaimed, "Mini Tex, you don't have to watch me get undressed." Mini Tex shook his head and said, "Sorry, Mr.

Pauly, the mustache made me think of a porno I was in during the '70s. Pauly shook his head and said, "I get that everywhere I go."

Lunch was served at the gigantic table made of oak and chairs that looked like thrones. The lunch was to die for. It was a homemade roll that looked like a large pizza, with a thirty-two-ounce homemade burger topped with a slab of bacon, a brick of cheese, French fries (homemade, of course), condiments of your choice, and for desert homemade pie a la mode.

After Lunch it was time for a cigar, which if you wanted, they would smoke it for you if you were too full to smoke. Mr. Pauly was heard to say, "You can't scare me!"

The hunting crew spent the time between lunch and dinner at the spa getting facials and massages.

"Time for dinner" came the shout as a dinner bell was rung.

It was a formal affair in which all guests were provided Tuxedos for the gala. Dinner was a thirty-two-once ribeye, potato, corn, salad, and more homemade pie a la mode. A fine red can of Bud was served to Mr. Pauly as he died and went to heaven. He was heard to say "What a place, Bud in Coors Country!"

When dinner was over the hunting group retreated to the den for an after-dinner smoke, brandy, and a discussion of the next day's hunt. They retired to their bedrooms, got into the silk PJs provided them by the ranch, and went to sleep in a king size bed while visions of elk danced in their heads.

The sun began to poke its head over the Rockies as the men finished their homemade breakfast of eggs, bacon, home fries, pancakes, sausage, OJ, and coffee. They were then taken to hollowed hunting grounds by limousine and dropped off at their private tree stands. The tree stands were no ordinary tree stands, they were actually tree houses. They were 2,000 square feet and had an elevator to get you up to the house. Each had running water, indoor plumbing, electric, heating and air conditioning, leather furniture, a kitchen, and a queen size bed to take a mid-day nap. The tree houses were stocked with food and beverages as well as a butler.

The houses had an enclosed patio around the house so you could walk around the house and kill elk with deadly accuracy, little effort, and no chance of burning any calories.

Well, our faithful group of tough hunters got their quota of elk and mule deer in about three hours. Really, how hard is it when they walk the elk and deer into your gun site? A crew then came from the limos, picked up the game, butchered it, freezer-wrapped and labeled it, put it into the home improvement magnate's new Ford F-750, and, most importantly, stocked his refrigerator with Bud for the ride home.

Mr. Pauly made it home safe and sound, came back to the Box and proclaimed "The Hunt is not for me if I have to burn a calorie."

Good day!

The Pick-up Artists

It is always a disaster to hear the love stories from the love-lorn, but it is worse when the stories involve Box regulars. This is a first-hand account witnessed by this reporter.

It is tough enough dealing with the fairer sex in private. However, at the Box, we are again privileged to witness some of the great romantics of our time. The time and paper it would take does not allow me to focus on all the painted masterpieces, so I will wet your pallet with a few of my favorites. I myself am no expert, since I was, oh, what's the right word, STUPID ENOUGH to put her name on the deed only for her to leave and take my dining room table. Although I have nowhere to eat, which is a good thing since I need to shed some tonnage, I was able to keep the house. So no one is exempt.

Where oh where to begin! I suppose from the top will do. A lonely Yankee fan, and yes, there are two, so I'll let you ponder which one this is, went on a date for the first time in a long time. He managed by the grace of God to have this woman say yes to the date. He picked her up in his 1957 Edsel and escorted her to an affair. The thought "liquor is quicker," flashed through his head and he began to ply rum and coke down her throat. Somewhere between twenty-seven and forty-seven, according to witnesses who have no clue.

The night came to a close and he took her home. The liquor began to dull her senses and she placed her hand on the thigh of this toupeed Yankee fan. His heart started to race, or in this man's case, walk at slow pace.

He was so shocked this woman has yet to call the cops he put his car in reverse and drove it into a wall. Upon further review, it came to light that the woman was not putting her hand on this man's thigh, but instead looking for a napkin he stole from the event because she was nauseous from the alcohol. There was no damage to the car because the owner, Captain Napkin, lined the bumper with napkins for just such an occasion. The building was not so lucky, as it had to be rebuilt. The Napkin told his insurance company not to pay because the plaza's owners had no business putting a building there. The Lexus Lawyer represents him.

Our second dating disaster was a classy affair. The Box's own fashion statement in pink pullover sweaters decided it was time to go on a conventional date. He decided a classy dinner and conversation would be nice for a change, instead of dinning with the Rug and scouring for napkins. The evening starts out smoothly: champagne, appetizers, four-course dinner, more champagne, dessert, and more champagne.

Then the conversation headed south as she babbled about her ex-boyfriend who is still married and she still loves and the tears started flowing. They not only pour from her tear ducts, but now our pink-sweater-wearing Yankee fan burst out in tears, sobbing uncontrollably as the reality of the situation hit him, that Captain Napkin did better on his date. It cost this Yankee fan 190 dollars for a miserable time and it cost the Rug a twenty-dollar donation for dinner and drinks and a quick thigh squeeze, only proving that while Cubs fans love the loveable losers, Yankee fans are just losers at love. Perhaps Yankee fans should stick to baseball, because the dating world is not their strong suit.

I had the unfortunate experience to witness a third account of a Box regular charm the opposite sex. Here is a personal account of this train wreck.

It's not often that women grace the Box, and when they do there is no shortage of brilliance. It amazes me that some of these guys managed to ever get a date, much less get married, but miracles do happen. I remember sitting in my usual chair and a striking woman showed up at the register. I struck up a conversation with her. The typical what do you do yada, yada, yada.

"I own a liquor store," came her response. All of sudden out of nowhere comes, "Ma'am, ma'am, ma'am, my friend Spanky Spankowitz owed a liquor store in 1966 during the Vietnam War and he did quite well for himself. He was able to buy my 1964 GTO with cash, and did anyone ever tell you that you are a seven and three-quarters out of ten?" She was stunned not only by the story but the scalding coffee he spilled on her.

I don't make them up, folks, I just report them.

Just when this reporter thought he had seen all there was to be seen in Box dating skills, I was sadly mistaken, as you'll see in these two sad but true incidents of how not to charm a woman.

Typically any male at the Box can use the restroom without anyone noticing. Unfortunately, females cannot. If you happen to be female and the pond maker is in, you have two choices: hold it or endure the inevitable. If you decide to run the gauntlet, you will hear a little squeaky voice yell out, "Look at the picture on the wall and think of me." Of course, not knowing what to expect, the unsuspecting female figures it out quickly enough and realizes her only choices is to stare at the horrible picture and face her fears.

They come out startled and are faced with the question, "Did you think of me when you saw my picture?" The shock is too great and no one has yet to answer.

Just when you think it cannot get worse, it does. An unknown customer's sister-in-law was visiting, telling a story of a dinner she threw when one of her friends got indignant with her brother-in-law. Of course the guys said they would have told her to "go fuck yourself," when one Box customer known for spillage tells her, "Have your brother-in-law blow smoke in her face." He then pointed to the bumper sticker that says "Cigar Smoke is an Idiot Repellant."

If that wasn't bad enough, he continued with, "You could have also told her that her deodorant isn't working."

I live in the TWILIGHT ZONE!

The brother-in-law looked at Sweet Lou, who looked back at him and said, "Why don't you blow that smoke at *him*. See if it works!"

So, ladies, as you can see, there is no hope!

No Salvation

The *Box Burns Gazette* has learned that the Box's own Sweet Lou is a dick. No, not a male sex organ, a private eye. This reporter was able to get ahold of his dick journal. NO, not porn, his private eye notes. He uses an alias so he can hide his true identity. Why, we don't know, since his true identity isn't worth hiding. So here it is, Sweetness's first case.

This is the city, Buffalo, New York. The city of good neighbors and one not so nice shopper. The names were changed because anyone who would want their real name used is an idiot.

It was Wednesday, December 21, and I was working the day watch, mainly because I work days. My partner's name is really not that important. My name is Fat Tuesday because I was born on Fat Tuesday, and mainly because I'm fat and I'm a private eye. A man in a Salvation Army Uniform walked in and introduced himself. He said his name was General Hill.

I said, "What could I do for you, Eisenhower?"

He looked at me strangely, shook his head, and proceeded to tell his tale. He said an unknown male entered his store and began casing the place. He looked at jackets, then picked up a Bills jacket and looked at the price. The price on the tag was thirty dollars. The male then picked up another item that was marked five dollars and switched the tags.

I asked him if he had seen this man before. The General replied never. I asked him did anyone see him do this. The General replied, "Yes, we have a witness and the video from our store."

I asked him who the witness was. The General replied Blind Pete. "What!" I said. He said, "Yes, Blind Pete. He has the eyesight of a bat and the hearing of a dog. He makes Chuck Norris look human."

I asked, "How can he possibly be a witness, he saw nothing." The General answered, "I know, but he heard him rip the tags off."

I lit my first cigar of the day and that did not go well. First, I don't smoke, and second, I had no matches. I chewed on the cigar, got sick, and asked to see the video.

I put the video in the DVD player it didn't work. Probably because it was VHS. Who has a VHS player nowadays? I went to the pawnshop and bought one for ten bucks. It looked familiar. It should have; it was mine. It was stolen from my house ten years ago.

I brought it back to my office, set it up, and watched the tape. The tape was useless. The first five minutes were so grainy that all you could see was the outline of a man; he looked like he was in a sand storm. It cleared up quickly after that. Only because someone had spliced a Clay-mation dramatization of the crime into the video.

Back to square one.

I told the General I'd get back to him if anything develops.

I drove to the scene of the crime and examined the store. I found out why the video was grainy. They had a bag over it. I asked the clerk why there was a bag over the camera. He said so the customers wouldn't know they were being taped. No one is putting rockets up in the air in this place. I shook my head, left the store, and drove to the cigar store to ponder my clues and the fifty-dollar retainer the General paid me. Then I weighed the pros and cons of getting my online degree in sociology.

I arrived at the Box twenty minutes later and bought an-other cigar. Since I chewed my first one I figured I'd smoke this one.

As I was smoking and mulling over my case a couple of young men came in and sat down next to me. I didn't pay any attention to them.

One of the guys begins to tell a story of how he saved him-self twenty-five dollars as well as avoiding breaking his hundred-dollar bill. His buddy said to him, "Do tell".

The guy said, "I was shopping for a jacket today at the Salvation Army and saw a Bills Jacket on the rack for thirty bucks. I had a hundred and five dollars in my pocket. A hundred-dollar bill and a five-dollar bill. So I didn't want to break up the hundred on a jacket. I saw a shirt on sale for five bucks and switched the tags. They don't call me 'the Switch' for nothing."

His buddy looked at him with disdain. He asked why he didn't buy one for him.

I was so shocked at my good fortune that I inhaled my cigar, gagged, and almost died of smoke inhalation. I was so overjoyed thinking of the twenty-five-dollar bonus the General would pay for solving the case in less than twenty-four hours and that I could buy the rest of my stolen goods back from the pawnshop.

I approached the two men and asked which one was Switch. He raised his hand and asked, "Who wants to know?"

I told him my name was Tuesday and that I was a private eye. Switch said to me, "So what do you want?" I told him that he was coming with me back to the store or I'd call the cops.

Switch slid back in his chair and said you got me and began to tell his side of the story. He told me he had a horrible upbringing and was taught by his evil step-family never ever buy retail when you can switch tags instead. He didn't even like the Bills.

We left the Box and drove to the Salvation Army store to meet with the General. The Switch told his sad tale to the General. The General, feeling charitable, felt for Switch.

I asked the General if he wanted to press charges. He said no. However, he had an idea to save the soul of one tormented Mr. Switch.

The case was solved in less than twelve hours, but I never collected my bonus. Yes, the General paid it. As I found myself counting my extra twenty-five bucks, I saw a Santa ringing a bell standing next to a red kettle, which was welded to the floor in the pawnshop. I wondered if it was Switch. I dropped my bonus into the kettle and heard Santa say, "Only big bills, sir."

I never did get my Atari or my Mr. Coffee back from that pawnshop.

Extermination Day

The day of reckoning arrived at the famous Pauly Pavilion during the first week of November, *Box Burns Gazette* has learned.

While falling asleep spooning his dog Winchester, Mr. Pauly heard a disturbing sound coming from the ceiling of the new addition to the Pauly Pavilion. At first Mr. Pauly thought it was the wind, but those thoughts were quickly dashed when he noticed a speck of sawdust stuck in his porn mustache.

The home improvement expert looked up and saw a mouse had gnawed through the new ceiling and gotten into the rafters. Mr. Pauly thought no problem as he went to the chemical closet and got a little d-CON. The d-CON was put in place and Mr. Pauly fell asleep spooning his dog.

The sun rose, touching the peaks of the mountains that surround the Pauly Pavilion, and the morning dew danced on the grass, creating a beautiful rainbow. Dazed by the lack of sleep since he came back from roughing it in the Rockies, Pauly rose from the bunk, pushed off the dog and began to sniff the wonderful aroma of bacon, eggs, and coffee permeating from the kitchen. "Jesse is up early and cooking already," Pauly exclaimed to himself, "this is going to be a good day. How wrong can one man be!"

As he entered the kitchen, the site of the mouse working the frying pan awed him. The mouse turned his head smiled, and it appeared to Mr. Pauly the mouse gave him the finger. He looked down at the table, saw d-CON on a plate with his hat on the seat and a mouse trap loaded with a Cuban cigar bought from his Cuban cigar connections Rooster and the Terrorist. Pauly thought to himself that this had to be a dream.

Oh no, *Box Burns* readers, it was not. The mouse did in fact give him the finger, ate his bacon and eggs, and then proceeded to kidnap Jesse and tie him up in the garage along with the goose.

Mr. Pauly began to stroke his mustache, which took several hours because his finger got entangled in the monstrosity. He needed to come up with a plan to rid the palace of the pesky rodent. As he paced the floor pondering his situation, he came upon a sight so sinister it would make the devil shudder. He looked on the floor saw a ransom note for Jesse. The mouse was on the recliner in a smoking jacket, smoking one of Jim's favorite cigars with a can of Bud in his other paw.

That was final straw. "Where is my gun," screamed Pauly as he read the ransom note for Jesse. All the mouse wanted was a brick of cheese and a box of cigars monthly. "I'll have to think about that," said Pauly. Now he began to get madder by the minute, thinking no mouse could beat him, he's killed bigger animals than this.

Shots rang out as Pauly fired at the mouse, a miss here a miss there, everywhere a miss, miss. Nothing, nada, no deal, the mouse escaped and was nowhere to be found. A few minutes later a feather from the goose was found by Pauly, not a good sign for the goose or Jesse. Pauly looked at the damage to his Pavilion and decided to call in an expert. He scanned his new Apple iPhone and found an exterminator, that being one Spankowitz Anchor, Globe, and Eagle Exterminators.

How many Spankowitzes can there be? He called the number as he saw the feathers pile up.

The phone rang and the voice on the other end said, "Spankowitz Anchor, Globe, and Eagle Exterminating, Sparky

Spankowitz speaking." Pauly took a shot and asked if he knew one Dave Masin.

"Hell yeah," yelled Sparky, "He and my brother Spanky made napalm together in the Marines, and not to mention they worked on tanks together and they're both deaf as posts. Well, Mr. Pauly, did Dave ever tell you the story of how they met President J.F.K. while making napalm? I love that story, I could listen to it a hundred times a day."

Pauly couldn't resist and said, "Well, take a ride to the Box, you'll hear it and hear it at least a hundred times."

Sparky told Pauly, "That Masin is one crazy bastard, you've got to hear his Marine tales about him and Spanky."

Pauly thought Sparky was a nut and had to cut him off. "Look, I have a mouse problem, can you help me?"

Sparky screamed, "Sure can, partner! I'll be there in an hour."

Pauly waited as the time passed slowly and almost passed out as he saw a surplus tank pull up with the words Spankowitz Exterminating painted on it. Sparky popped out of the turret and started yelling, "Where is the little bastard, I'll blow him out of the house." After Sparky calmed down he saw Pauly staring at the tank totally stunned and a teardrop gently falling to the ground. Armageddon has come to the Pauly Pavilion.

"Well, Mr. Pauly, this reminds me of my days in Nam hunting Kong. You know, that's what we used to call them in country in '65. I was there with my older brother Spunky Spankowitz surrounded by those slant-eye bastards. We were out of ammo and all we had left were four napalm canisters that Spanky and Masin gave us as a going-to-Nam present. Well, let me tell you, me and Spunky fired off the napalm and fried those Commie Bastards to kingdom come and that's what is going to happen to your mouse, Mr. Pauly."

Oh God, Pauly thought. First he saw Sparky grab a Springfield rifle from the turret, put in the powder, and aim for the mouse. Sparky squeezed the trigger, nothing. Then all of sudden a fire ball exploded from the rifle, turning Sparky's face black. "Damn, I hate when that happens," yelled Sparky. "I should have listen to Masin and filled it to the brim with powder, that man sure knows his weapons, don't he, Mr. Pauly?"

The mouse laughed.

"Well, don't that beat all," yelled Sparky. "That mouse has laughed its last laugh."

Pauly looked up at the turret and saw Sparky loading the barrel with napalm.

"Nooooooo!" Pauly yelled, but it was too late.

The napalm blaze was everywhere; the pavilion, the kitchen, the garage, Jesse, and the goose all gone, burning like a five-alarm fire. Then out of the ashes, his beard charred, holding a dazed but a still alive goose in his arms, Jesse emerged. "Did you get the mouse, Jim?" asked Jesse.

"I don't know!" said a crying Jim Pauly, "ask that nut Sparky."

"Sure did, partner," yelled Sparky. "You can't beat napalm!"

All of a sudden the tank began to move and chase Sparky all around the destroyed estate. As he looked back he saw the mouse in the turret giving him the finger, yelling, "you missed me in Nam and you missed me here, asshole!"

Movie Madness

A certain retired financial broker thought that it would be a good idea to take two of his five grandchildren to the movies on Saturday afternoon. It turned out to be an adventure in babysitting for his grandkids. What started out as a typical Saturday drive turned into a kid's nightmare.

While driving to the theatre, a normally five-minute drive took an hour. The kids, bored to tears from hearing an hour's worth of "my pond, my pond," begged their grandfather to stop, but to no avail.

Thankfully a police officer pulled up next to their car and saw the kid's plight. The officer pulled the car over and was amazed at the number of curbs the Box customer hit when attempting to move to the right. The cop asked if there was a problem.

The Box customer replied, "No, Officer, nothing here."

Then he asked the kids and they pleaded with the officer to take them to the movies so they would not have to hear about the pond ever again. The officer told the obsessive grandfather to cease and desist with the pond or he would run him in. The kids cheered. The cop also asked one of the kids to drive so there would be at least one person in the car who could see over the steering wheel. The kids laughed and the older grandson took the wheel and got them to the movies in five minutes.

The trio approached the ticket booth and gramps asked for three children's tickets. The clerk looked down at the three and said which one is the adult. The kids laughed, pointed, and said the pissed-off one. The clerk said twenty-five dollars. The Box customer pulled out a twenty-dollar bill and said close enough. The clerk was stunned as the unknown Box customer took the tickets and proceeded to the candy counter. At the counter he ordered a small popcorn and coke for the kids. The clerk said thirty dollars. Gramps flipped.

He yelled, "I could get a dinner, dessert, and a lidless coffee at the Park Club for that much!" The manager heard this and told gramps that when they start showing movies at the Club let him know, enjoy the show.

The show he took the kids to was called *Rio*, about two macaws that fall in love and fly away to live happily ever after. The trio sat behind a group of Taliban tribesmen wearing turbans. The grandfather leaned over to the tribesmen and said, "Can you take off the turbans, we can't see a thing." The tribesman got up and started to scream Allah and threatened to blow up the theatre. The kids screamed please pull the cord so we don't have to hear about the pond.

At the end of the movie the kids were stunned to see their grandfather crying. The grandfather asked the kids if they liked the movie. The kids replied that they fell asleep five minutes in and would have rather seen *Hangover 2* and not some lame animated movie.

As they were leaving the kids looked at each other and hatched a plan because they couldn't take another minute in that car. They told their grandfather to go ahead; they called a cab.

Jim Pauly's *The Wild Kingdom*

Yes, *Gazette* readers, just when you thought we had have run out of stories, Box regulars come through and provide more ammunition than necessary. There is something to be said for hanging out in a target-rich environment.

Two Box customers have started a new show called *The Wild Kingdom.* Your host is Jimmy "Big Rig" Pauly, and Dave "Even if you did hear it I'm going to repeat it" Masin appears as your color commentator.

Here is a transcript of the first episode.

Jimmy: Hello out there, hunters, I am your host, Jimmy "Big Rig" Pauly, and welcome to our first show of the new season.

Dave: It's our first show.

Jimmy: I'm sure, fans, you are all wondering how I got the name "Big Rig." Well, I'm going to tell you. I gave it to myself when I got my CDL. That's a big 10-4 for all you truckers out there. I'll be the man in the F-750 on the 219 driving with my pant leg rolled up so I don't kill myself when I get out of truck. I did that once in front of my thirty employees they all laughed and now I'm a mom and pop operation. I even fired my own son. If mom doesn't watch out, I'll just be a pop operation. Keep on talking, Annie dear.

Dave: Gave himself the name and drives an F-750. Did you hear that? Let me tell them how you fell out of your truck, Jimmy. You see, folks, Jimmy had his pant leg roll up and when he got out of his truck he began to roll his pant leg down with his other foot, got it tangled in the pant leg and fell off the truck. Isn't that right, Jimmy? You have to admit it; Jimmy here tells a great story.

Jimmy: You know, when you go out in the woods you like to be comfortable, don't you?

Dave: You like to be comfortable.

Jimmy: Anyway, I like my tighty-whities when I go out into the woods, and you know how I like them?

Dave: You know how he likes them?

Jimmy: He's not the best color man in the business for nothing, sports fans. Anyway, as I was saying, I have my wife sew up the sack so I don't fall out, you know what I'm saying? Come on guys, there ain't nothing more embarrassing than having your equipment fall out while you are hunting and your Indian guide laughs so hard that he can't guide anymore because of what you're packing.

Dave: His wife sews his sack up and he is packing. I love a man who packs.

Jimmy: So as I was saying, that's why my wife sews up my pouch sack, and yours should too.

Dave: Fellas, your wives should sew your sacks, too.

Jimmy: Well, hunters, I have some great stories to tell you about hunting deer and elk. As you all know I own a pavilion down in Franklinville and I hunt.

Dave: Raises deer and hunts.

Jimmy: Thanks, Dave. I was in my tree stand adjusting my sack because my wife sewed my sack to the tighty-whities while I was sleeping, when I saw this ten-point rack behind a tree.

Dave: Wife sewed his sack and he saw a ten-point rack. Hey, I made a rhyme. You know, back at Wilson High School in 1957, I was in the ninth grade and I had to write a poem on hunting. My ninth grade teacher, Miss Spankowitz, an elderly lady with gray hair down to her—

Jimmy: That's enough. Concentrate, remember your napalm days.

Dave: Did I ever tell you I made orange Jell-O? Me and Spanky....

Jimmy: A million times, Dave, focus! Anyway, I saw the ten-pointer behind the tree. Then he moved out from the tree with a branch under his leg. I took aim and fired, killing the deer instantly. I climbed down, examined the deer, and saw that it wasn't a branch, it was a crutch. And then I looked at the rack, and on that rack was a handicapped sticker. I had killed a previously wounded deer.

Dave: Deer moved and he shot it. The deer was handicapped and Jimmy here killed it. Isn't that the funniest thing ever?

Jimmy: The adventure doesn't end there. While on my property hunting that elusive healthy four-legged deer with no medical assistance, I spotted out of the corner of my mustache a rack that was so huge that it made the stripper Candy Samples jealous.

Dave: A big rack that made a stripper jealous...Tom, Tom, Tom...did you hear that one?

Jimmy: As I was saying before my tape recorder interrupted, I saw this deer by a big old wagon wheel – what a wagon wheel was doing out on my property, I don't know. So I took aim and fired. It was a great kill shot. I approached the deer and the look of shock came over me. What I thought was a wagon wheel was in fact a wheel from an old wheel chair donated by one George Costanza to help the crippled deer fund. Can you believe my luck?

Dave: Saw a wheel and a deer, shot the deer, killed a wheel chair. How is that for shooting, folks? Like my old friend Frank Tully use to say back in 1968, 'Get yourself a gun because we are going to have to protect ourselves from them liberal bastards.'

Jimmy: As you can imagine, I've been banned from hunting in New York State by the Why Can't You Shoot a Healthy Deer Foundation, liberal pieces of crap. Anyway, I took my shotgun and hunting skills to Colorado and hired an Indian guide named Six Beers. I don't know how he got the name, but I'm sure I'd find out.

Dave: He was banned from hunting in NY State, went to Colorado and got an Indian guide. You know, Jim, my great, great, great, great Aunt was married to an Indian. She sure was. You know those beads that the Indians got for Manhattan? Well, her husband, whose name was One Who Makes Bad Deal, gave them to her for a wedding gift. Look, I've got them right here. Shit, I dropped them down the sewer. They were going to give me twenty-four dollars and trinkets on *Pawn Stars* and they had to be worth at least twenty-four thousand. I figured that was a good deal after conferring with One Who Makes Bad Deal's relatives who I found on incestory.com.

Jimmy: That's great, Dave, can I please continue? I only have so many years left! So I'm up in the Rockies with my guide Six Beers and he's pointing out deer left and right, but I couldn't see a thing. He would point right and I'd look left, he'd point left and I'd look right. Finally he just said your other right, Mr. Pauly. I thanked him and he point out another deer and I'd say where, again he would tell me my other right. I'd look and couldn't see a thing.

He muttered something under his breath. 'Of all the people I get to guide I wind up with Mr. Magoo.' I offered Six Beers a Bud, he says no. Funny thing, every time I offer this guy a beer he says no. How the hell did he get this name Six Beers?

Dave: Doesn't know right from left, pisses off guide. Ha-ha Mr. Magoo. Offers guide a beer, he says no.

Jimmy: Finally! Six Beers gives me a pair of binoculars the size of the Hubble telescope and I see the deer going back and forth at steady pace. I take aim and fire. I shout, 'I got him, damn I'm good,' and offered Six Beers another Bud, but he said no. We get down to the area where I shot the deer and see flames and smoke billowing into the air. Not only did I miss the deer, but I hit his gas-powered Rascal scooter in the gas tank and blew the deer and scooter to kingdom come. There was nothing I could say. I turned to Six Beers and said, 'Why did you tell me to shoot him?' and offered him a Bud. Six Beers said, 'I told you not to shoot! That is our deer rehab farm, and why do you keep offering me Bud?' I said, 'All trip you have been talking into my bad ear and I couldn't hear a word. In fact, I couldn't hear a fog horn if I had my head in the cone of the horn. Also, Six Beers, I find you quite rude.' He said, 'How is that, Mr. Pauly?' So I said, "Well, all day I've been offering you a Bud to drink and all day you have refused. Isn't that a little rude?' Six Beers replied, 'Why are you offering me beer? All day you have been calling me Six Beers! My name, dammit, is Six *Bears*!' All I could say is oops wrong ear! Now I'm banned from all Colorado hunting grounds. Dave, where did you get those hearing aids?

Dave: WHAT!

Be sure to tune in for the next episode of Jimmy "Big Rig" Pauly's *The Wild Kingdom*, live on the *Gazette Cable News* channel. Unless of course you don't get *Gazette Cable News*, which is the case for just about all of America.

The Rug's Lost Heir Found at the Box

An interesting development took place as Jimmy the Rug's lost heir was found by a curious gumshoe named Sweet Lou. The *Box Burns Gazette* interviewed Sweetness to find out the details of this heart-warming story.

Here is Sweetness telling his tale of loss then found and hopefully lost again.

I was sitting in the Box enjoying a relaxing moment as the former Marine found another victim from the great country of Canada. It was quiet; a small crowd was sitting in the lounge with Sam and Mike working. Mike was a new hire with a connection to the owner's son. The Yankee game was on, but I didn't care because I didn't have to listen to any Marine deer games.

I was able to sit back and listen for the possibility of a story coming my way. I figured, small crowd, and how many Masin stories can there possibly be left in the holster? Of course, we all know the answer to that one, but I digress. The game went along at the pace of a handicapped snail. The only two watching were me and the employees.

Then out of the blue came the most disturbing sound I've ever heard. The high-pitched voice came from behind the counter, yelling 'SWISHHHHHER' like a gay salsa dancer flapping his wrist as the Yankee slugger hit a garden-variety home run. A sound came from behind counter, the likes of which only one human being can make, sounds that only Jimmy the Rug can make: the sounds of him making love to a Milanovich's pizza. It then dawned on me; all the clues fell into place, the prodigal son was found after all these years. The heir apparent for Jimmy the Rug has come down from the mountain and will take his place as a Box irritant during baseball season.

I learned the Rug will leave his prized Yankee road uniform and napkin collection to the newly found heir, now crowned Jimmy the Rug Jr, or just plain JTR Jr, all thanks to the most effeminate cheer you will ever hear in your lifetime – SWISHHHHERRRR!

A side note: Jimmy the Rug and Jr were caught on Box security cameras doing the wave and yelling "SWISHHERRRR!" and then hugging each other as the original Rug fell asleep in Jr's arms after the cheer.

Sterling the Pot

The Box's own walking and talking human non-history fact book reared its .44 caliber Magnum and took aim on a small should-have-known-it-was-coming-but-didn't-expect-it group. The group, consisting of an unknown pizza shop owner, the oldest student at UB, and the late-night purveyor of afterhours, were discussing college tuitions and the debt it puts many students in.

All of a sudden, lying in wait, sat the dreaded gunslinger of useless facts and history. He fired a shot across the bow. "Did you know that a famous actor named Sterling Moss worked on the fishing boats in Massachusetts and paid his way through college?"

The gunslinger realized his useless fact was even more useless than usual when he fired off the wrong name. He corrected himself, saying, "It wasn't Sterling Moss, he was a race car driver in the fifties or sixties, I think his name was Sterling Marlin, did you know he was a Marine? No, he was another racecar driver."

The group responded, "What the hell does this have to do with what we're talking about?"

This did not stop the false-fact-throwing gun fighter, as he continued like a salmon swimming upstream to spawn. "No, no, I think his name was Sterling Sharpe, and he became an officer in the Marines."

The late-night purveyor said, "Are you out of your fucking mind, Sterling Sharpe was a football player. Are you sure you don't mean Sterling Silver, and that he paid his way through college by polishing anything silver?"

By this time the group had moved on to a new subject. However, the relentless fact-flinger continued his lethal deluge of non-relevancy. He jumped out of seat like a contestant on *Pass Word* and yelled, "I got it. It was Sterling Hayden!"

The group yelled, "Who the hell is Sterling Hayden?"

The reply from the pesky pun slinger, "The actor, he played in many westerns." Once again, another useless fact of history rained down upon the group as the pun slinger put another notch in his spill-proof mug.

Just so you can rest easy, Sterling Hayden played Captain McCluskey in *The Godfather*.

Math Miscalculation

Well, loyal readers, it is certainly the month of Jimmy "Big Rig" Pauly. He has made the *Box Burns Gazette* a record number of times for a four-week period as a main story. This week we find our loveable leading story-maker doing math at his kitchen table with an unknown guest believed to be that world-renowned mathematician's brother from *A Perfect Mind*, Sine Cosine Spankowitz, the cousin of Sparky, Spunky, and Spanky, drinking Bud and trying to put rockets in the air.

Let's take a sneak-peek at the conversation.

Big Rig: I wonder, how many beers did we drink in the ten years I've owned this property?

Sine: Let's see, Big Rig, if we drank a thousand beers a year…nope, nope, nope, make that ten thousand a year times ten years, that would be a one million beers. Let's write the Budweiser Company and maybe they will give us more to drink and a few math problems on the side.

Big Rig: Good Idea.

After sending in their letter of their crowning achievement, Sine and Big Rig waited for a response from Anheuser-Busch. A few weeks later a response came.

Dear Big Rig and Sine,

Thank you for the letter stating how much you liked Bud. However, perhaps, you should write when you are capable of doing math. You see, gentlemen, 10,000 times ten is 100,000, not one million. So we cannot assist you in your goal to build a tribute to napalm out of Bud cans. Besides, what moron talks about napalm and wants to build a tribute to it? Also, please refrain from ever drinking our product again, you are banned. NO BUD FOR YOU!

Respectfully,

Augustus Bush

Upon receiving the letter, Big Rig was heard saying, "Dammit, Sine, I told you it was one trillion cans, you never listen to me."

Sine Cosine responded, "You are so right, it was a trillion. I didn't carry the zeroes."

Next time you need help adding something up, be sure to ask anyone other than these two mathematical wizards.

My Vacation: What a DRAGnet

A loyal box customer recently returned from the first vacation with his new girlfriend. When pressed for details, he refused to spill the beans. Well, readers, the *Box Burns Gazette* has obtained a copy of his vacation journal. Yes, we agree with you, who actually is lame enough to keep a vacation journal these days? This reporter presents you with that journal here, unedited. Enjoy!

This is the city, Portland. No, the other Portland. Maine. Population 66,000. Known as the blueberry capital of the world, and now, the blue-balls capital of the world. Portland is also known for its scenic beauty, fresh lobster, and rustic bed and breakfasts. The perfect romantic getaway, unless you've been "mushed." That's where I fit in. My name is Kevin, and I carry a grudge.

It was Wednesday, May 22, 12 p.m. We were on our way to the airport. My companion's name was Noway, and there was no way to foresee the events of this trip that were about to unfold.

We arrived in Portland at 2 p.m. The new pilot, the guy in row twenty, finally landed the plane. Probably because we were out of fuel.

We got our luggage. Mine was lost, she got and extra bag.

I hailed a cab; it drove by. I hailed another cab; he turned off his light. I finally stepped in front of one; it hit me.

The ambulance got us to the bed and breakfast at 2:45 p.m. The clerk asked my name. I gave it. She couldn't find it.

3:35 p.m. we entered the room. She turned up the heat. It was not what I expected: It was the thermostat. I began to sweat, she put on a Parka.

5:45 p.m. it was dinnertime. We went to the best restaurant in town. It was closed. We went to Joe's Diner. She ordered the bisque; I ordered a lobster roll. There was no lobster in the roll. I had a roll.

6 p.m. we walked off dinner. We crossed the street. 7 p.m. it was time for bed. She turned on the TV. I was expecting porn. She put on QVC.

8 p.m. she bought six flannel pajamas. They were delivered in five minutes. She put them on. I was still sweating.

9 p.m. we went to bed. I put my arm around her. She screamed, "Don't make me get out the tape measure."

She slept. I watched *Funny Girl*.

Thursday, May 23, 5:45 a.m. She still slept, I went for breakfast. I went to Joe's.

Best place in town for breakfast. It was closed. The best restaurant in town was open. They don't serve Breakfast.

6:45 a.m. still hungry, I bought a paper. It was yesterdays.

9:45 a.m. she was still asleep, tape measure in her hand. I called a cab. The ambulance picked me up. The fare was seven hundred dollars. The driver gave me a roll. It had lobster in it.

10:45 a.m. the driver got lost. He was from out of town.

11 a.m. I was dropped off at the art gallery. I paid twenty-five bucks to get in. There was no art, they were painting the walls. I watched paint dry.

11:45 a.m. I went next door to the science museum. They had Art. Art was the security guard.

4:45 p.m. I went to a lighthouse. The light was out and it was dim.

6:45 p.m. she was still asleep. The tape measure was in her hand. The room was still ninety degrees. Room service brought in sand, palm trees, and a camel.

7:45 p.m. Joe's Diner. She had eggs. I had the seafood platter, it was tuna fish from a can in the shape of the letter C.

9 p.m. she was tired. The room cooled down. It was eighty-nine degrees. The camel was wearing a sweater.

I pulled back the sheets. There was an electrical tape dividing line in the middle of the bed.

I got into bed. She said, "If you put your arm around me, you'll need a passport." I had one with me. It was expired.

She was cold. I was sweating. Her temperature was twenty degrees. Mine, 98.6.

I was hot and cold at the same time. I wore socks and a sun visor to bed. She slept and I watched *Sleepless in Seattle*.

Friday 7 a.m. I woke up. A Nomad was milking the camel. She was still asleep. I went to Joes. I ordered eggs and toast. I got a roll. It had lobster in it.

8 a.m. in front of the B and B. The ambulance picked me up. There was a patient in it. We split the fare. He went to the hospital. I went whale watching.

I should have gone to the hospital. The boat was waiting. It held two. Where I come from they call it a canoe. We rowed out to see the whales.

It took eight hours to get there. It cost me three hundred dollars. There were no whales. By the time we got there they had already ate, played, and swam north.

I saw Noway on a charter boat coming back to shore. She showed me a picture of the whales she saw. I showed her a picture of a cod. She left.

I hit my guide with an oar. We split the ride back to the hospital. He had a concussion. I had a rap sheet.

9 p.m. I was bailed out by Dog the Bounty Hunter. I lent him money to bail me out.

10 p.m. I got back to the room. She was asleep. The Great Wall of China was now in Portland, Maine. It was down the middle of my bed.

She slept. I watched *Crouching Tiger, Hidden Dragon*. I now speak Chinese.

6:45 a.m. Time to go home. I checked out. I got charged extra for the wall and the camel. I also got the bill from QVC for the PJ's.

7 a.m. we waited outside. It was rainy and clear all at the same time. I got wet, and it was clear I got none. She had an umbrella from QVC.

The ambulance was waiting. I rode in the front. She fell asleep on the gurney.

7:30 a.m. we arrived at the airport. They checked our luggage. They checked hers. They threw out mine.

8 a.m. we got on the plane. The pilot greeted me. It was the guy in row twenty. He had an instruction manual.

10 a.m. my brother picked me up at the airport. He doesn't drive. The ambulance driver's brother picked us

up. He got lost. He was from out of town. He was from Portland. No! Not Maine, Oregon!

We dropped off Noway. She said call me. I said, "No Way!" She said, "What?" I said again, "NO Way!" She said, "What?"
I went to a Greek restaurant and had a Spanish omelet.

In a moment, the results of my vacation: It cost me a one thousand dollars. I had no sex. I spent fifty bucks on chick flicks. I did not see a whale, but I did see Art. He looked good in his uniform. I bought a blow up doll!

Wheel of Misfortune

Well, Box fans, it is truly an honor to be reporting from the set of *Wheel of Fortune*. It is a rare event that three contestants are from the same city and frequent the same cigar establishment on the *Wheel of Fortune*, and I'm happy to say I witnessed history.

Here is that glimpse into said history with a transcript from the show.

Pat: Welcome to *Wheel of Fortune*. I'm your host, Pat Sajack, and this is our lovely letter turner, Vanna White. Today's guests are certainly a fine group of men from quite different walks of life. So without further ado, let's meet them. Our first contestant is a home improvement expert and world-renowned hunter of crippled animals. He has five three-legged deer to his credit, one wounded Elk, and one hunting guide, all documented kills. Say hello to Jimmy "Big Rig" Pauly.

Big Rig: Pat, I would just like to say I only wounded the guide and that was only because I couldn't see him. I'm just saying.

Pat: Thanks for clearing that up, Big Rig. Our next contestant is a former Marine and napalm specialist and all around good guy, Dave Masin. So, Dave, tell us about your napalm days.

Big Rig: Bad question, Pat.

Dave: Pat, Pat, Pat, as it said on my fifty-page application, I did see the president, one JFK, in the middle of the ocean and he waved to us. I was with my friend and fellow private, Spanky Spankowitz. His brother Sparky is an Exterminator and did a hell of a job at Jim Pauly's pavilion. Ain't that right, Jim?

Pat: Thanks, Dave, we only have half an hour. Our third and final contestant is a nursery and Top Soil owner, John Crantzy. I have to ask, John, was that you waving to Dave and Spanky in the middle of the Ocean?

JFC: No, Pat, I was only five at the time and was thinking of ways to bomb those Russian bastards. It would have worked, too, if my father had let me play with the fertilizer. I hate them Russians.

Pat: Ok, folks, we have quite a group here. Let's play *Wheel of Fortune!* Ok, your first clue is Lenai, five letters. John, you go first. Spin the wheel!

Pat: Five hundred dollars, your first letter is...

JFC: Just let me say this, Pat, those commie bastards are everywhere, look at your first clue: Lenin. Onbelievable!

Pat: No, it's not Lenin, its Lenai. It's Hawaiian. It's like veranda.

JFC: Again with the Russian words. Vodka. Nice. Ok, Pat, here we go M, as in Urban Meyer.

Pat: Sorry, no M. Dave, your spin.

Dave: Did I ever tell about the time I had my teeth removed? It's a great story.

Pat: Just the letter, Dave, please!

Dave: M, please.

Pat: John already said M.

Dave: I didn't hear him! You know, Pat, I lost my hearing.

Pat: Dave, enough!

Big Rig: My spin, Past?

Pat: It's Pat, Jim, not past.

Big Rig: I know, the s is silent. My god, no one speaks English around here except for me and Crantzy! I'll take a P.

Dave: Pat, Pat, Pat, did I ever tell you the time I had to take a Pee and the Box's door was locked? Whew, that was a close one!

Pat: No, Dave, tell me later. One P, there is a P, Big Rig.

Big Rig: C, Past.

Pat: It's Pat, and there is one C.

Big Rig: H, *Pat.* Is that better, you baby?

Pat: Yes! And there is one H.

Big Rig: U, please.

Pat: No U. JFC, your turn.

JFC: I'd like to buy a vowel and solve the puzzle. I'd like an O, Pat.

Pat: For the win and $10,000, solve the puzzle, John!

JFC: Ohio State.

Pat: My God, where did you get that from?

JFC: Pat, how stupid are you? There was an O in it and everyone knows that it stands for Ohio State. What's wrong with you! Damn Russians can't even spell Ohio!!

Pat: Dave, it's your turn.

Dave: I'd like to solve the puzzle!

Pat: Go ahead.

Dave: The answer is Pontiac, Pat.

Pat: No, Pontiac is wrong and it's seven letters, not five. My God! Where did you get that from?

Dave: Well, my first car was a 1964 GTO and it was made by Pontiac, and since I saw the P, C, and O, what else could it be? Would you like to hear about the time I got it up to 130 miles per hour?

Pat: Ok, Big Rig, it's up to you, guess one letter and you win.

Big Rig: Ok, Past! I would like a T, and the answer is PORTCH.

Pat: I'm sorry, there was no T, even though you solved the puzzle, you win nothing. There is no T in Porch.

Big Rig: There is too. Just ask my wife, she'll tell you!

Pat: Ok, Jim, I will. Ann?

Ann: WHO IS THAT MAN?

Pat: Well, folks, that's all for tonight's' show. Please tune in tomorrow when we have three contestants who can actually spell!

Self-diagnosis for Beginners

Perhaps you are wondering about the title of this little yarn. Fear not, loyal readers, as this reporter takes you on an adventure of diagnosis, denial, and disaster to unfold the true meaning of the title. It is with great relief that I get to write this and not an obituary for one of Box regular.

It was an unusually warm winter's day in Buffalo, snow nowhere in sight, and in walked a youthful man in his forties wearing a ninety-two-year-old's body. He shuffled over to the cigars to look for one to purchase and let out a scream as the one he has between his fingers torched his smoking hand. As he screamed he startled one Mr. Masin, who, as usual, has a drink in one hand and a story everyone has heard before coming from his mouth.

First, the fact that he heard something is a miracle in itself – which by the way is the second miracle of this story – and as no shock to anyone, he spilled his drink. But with true Marine gung-ho, he finished his story and promptly began another one on the virtues of the AK-47 and the pros and cons of having an insane dog.

However, let's bring you back to the real subject of this story: The man, the myth, and the non-medical doctor is none other than Mr. Milanovich, whose motto is, "If I haven't worked eighty hours this week I'm not working."

As he shuffled over to find a chair that may resemble a hospital bed, the regulars inquired, "Mr. M, are you all right?"

The reply, "Yeah, yeah, it's only a head cold."

"Really, you're shaking like Crantzy hunting for a candy bar, cheesecake, or something with enough sugar in it for his tooth to make Cuba a financial power."

"I'm fine," came the retort from Mr. M. A concerned regular asked him if he had eaten.

"Yeah, I had a potato chip for dinner, I'm good."

The saga went on for another week and no Mr. M in the house. People were worried because most ninety-year-old men on oxygen with a walker and a certified nurse's aide helping them look more vibrant than Mr. Milanovich looked that week.

As Box regulars sat pondering the whereabouts of Milanovich, in walked Mr. Cavanaugh. He reported that Milanovich is at home in bed recovering from an unknown illness. Mr. Cavanaugh said that Milanovich's doctor wanted him to go to the hospital, but he refused, telling his doctor the following, "Look, Doc, unlike you, I have no medical degree and have never been a doctor or even practiced, but I'm not going to the hospital based on my findings on the World Wide Web site www.hydrogenperoxide.org.net.com. After reading the site's many articles from well-unknown doctors from the medical hot bed of that little nation of Nepal on the miracles of modern hydrogen peroxide's strength on all known illnesses, I think I'll sit home, rest, and mix a batch of hydrogen peroxide and Kool-Aid. I'll be right as rain thanks to those two medieval pharmacists Rooster Wilson and Navy Otter Gavigan."

Two weeks had passed before a worn-looking Milanovich walked into the Box to proclaim he was as healthy as Whitney Houston swimming laps in her bathtub. Milanovich looked so sick the dead avoided him. Milanovich left early that night and was a no-show on his usual Sunday night visit to the Box. The regulars were so worried about him that they had the store's Marine tracker, one Mr. Masin, go out to see if he could find him.

They waited anxiously until Mr. Masin returned seven hours later. Mr. Masin stated, "This was the toughest case I ever had. I tried tracking him through the snow and couldn't. Since it hadn't snowed all winter I got lost and found Captain Napkin in Wegmans instead. Then I ran into the gentleman who bought my 1964 GTO and reminisced about that. Did you guys know that he became a Pontiac car salesman thanks to my GTO?"

"Dave," a shout came from the group. "FOCUS. What about Milanovich?"

"Well, fellas, this is where it gets interesting." Dave slid to the edge of his seat ready to tell the world of his exploits. "After I got lost, I thought, what would General Patton do? So I went over to the deli section and slapped a deli worker in the face who was crying because he cut his finger, screaming at him, 'I'm not going to have you crying in this deli over a paper cut, disgracing the other brave deli workers who have given their blood for kosher meats without so much as sick call. You're fired.' It was at this point the deli manager came over with the police and had me escorted off the premises. All I heard him say to the police – and it's a miracle I heard that – was 'He doesn't even work here!' So then I gave up and came back to the Box to tell everyone what happened."

So, Mr. Cavanaugh to the rescue! He called Milanovich's wife and found out that he was in the hospital being treated by a real doctor with real medicine.

Though Milanovich was close to visiting St. Peter at the pearly gates – and was rejected because he wasn't healthy enough to be dead – he is still with us and we love him, which is miracle number two. You figure out which one is the miracle; that we love him or that he is still with us.

Fish Fried

Gazette readers, I'm sure you have all heard the term Bad Check. Well, this reporter has the inside scoop of how a good check went bad.

It was a cold, beautifully clear winter's night when Sweet Lou arrived at the Box to relax and have a nice cigar, when he remembered – thanks to the notice sent to him by the Knights of Columbus – his annual dues were, excuse the pun, DUE. Sweetness put the check into his wallet thinking he could save himself time and trouble by giving it to one Jim Pauly, who, by the way, was attending a Knights meeting the following week. Lou thought it was a great idea, he'd save the stamp, put more postal workers out of a job, and have his dues in on time for a change.

So much for that bright idea. A coaching colleague of Lou's once said as they were arguing over a free agent prospect, "Louis, if you are so fucking smart, how come you are not rich?" Truer words were never spoken as Lou saw the fruits of his labor and what he thought was a good idea go down the drain. He received a "This is your second and last chance to get your dues in or you will be tossed from the Knights" notice. A puzzled look crossed his face and he thought maybe Jim forgot, so he called him to remind him again.

Sweet Lou placed the unfortunate call and asked him if he remembered to hand in his check for the Knights. The silence was deafening as he heard him shuffling papers around like a manic blackjack dealer reshuffling six decks with one hand. Then he heard, "Well, there seems to be a slight problem."

"Really!" Came Lou's response, "you forgot to hand in the check, didn't you?"

Then came the sound of slight laughter and, "I'll hand it in Friday during the fish fry."

The fish fry is where Jim can be found every Friday cooking fish for the Knights Friday Fish Fry. Surprise number one is that Jim remembered to hand in the check. To no one's surprise is what happened to said check. It was brought to Sweet Lou's attention that instead of paying his dues for the year, he was the happy owner of three nine-dollar fish fries which came to, if you do the math, twenty-seven dollars. If you do Jim's math, it's thirty-five dollars.

So instead of being an honorary Knight, Lou is now the proud owner of three fish fries, which he did not get to eat. He also had the privilege of tipping no one in particular EIGHT DOLLARS for nothing.

Needless to say, he is now on the Knights' best customer and tipper list, and unfortunately excommunicated from the Knights. But on the bright side, any time he wants a non-existent fish fry he has the privilege of paying nine dollars for an empty box, saying, "Here's a ten, boys. Keep the change," and the added bonus of hearing Jim "Copernicus" Pauly saying "look, another two-dollar tip!"

The Mashattan Project

During the big one, WWII, The United States was in the midst of the Great War and was trying to end it as quickly as possible. The government got all the great scientific minds together and decided to create a secret weapon. This plan was called the Manhattan Project. It was so secret that only the scientists and highly placed Army, Navy, OSS, and government officials knew the true nature of the project.

Let's now fast forward to the year 2012 of our Lord and take you to the secret laboratory of one Box regular, whom shall remain nameless and kept unknown. However, a well-placed Navy Otter has discovered a possible leak in this Box regular's inner circle. A disgruntled former Marine named Spanky Spankowitz let it slip while he and the covert Navy Otter were having coffee at a local bistro – at which, by the way, the Otter stuck Spankowitz with the bill as he conveniently left his wallet in his Navy Seal uniform. Spankowitz revealed this unknown Box regular is about to embark on a new business so secret the owner himself is not sure what it is.

The news got the Box regulars' minds revving with all sorts of ideas. This former Marine is so tight-lipped that we all want to know where this well-known unknown Marine is and what have you done with him.

This business plan is so unique to the business world the Navy Otter, a UBS retired V.P., is waiting for word of it so he can advise his clients not to buy. This business plan consist of telling no one what he is doing or selling. In fact, we are not sure if he knows what he is selling, it is so secret.

Many ideas have come forth, and I will share a few:

- A book of names and dates that no one cares about.
- A 1964 GTO picture book.
- A book of guns, guns, guns, and by the way, more guns.
- The spillers guide called *Spilling for idiots*.
- A how-to book on how to let someone tell their story while you do it for them.
- Trivial-no-one-cares-about Pursuit.
- An autobiography titled *Blink If I'm Lying*.
- The napalm maker's vacation guide where you can visit the Napalm Museum, find out how it's made, and actually visit places where it has been used.

As history repeats itself, we will just have to wait until the napalm is dropped to find out what this endeavor is. In all honesty, we all wish this secret Box customer the best of luck in his new business and hope his dream comes true and becomes his cash cow.

Out-Foxed

The Box's regular customer base has many talented people with all types of knowledge and skill. So they claim. Some are great builders, businessmen, athletes, writers, and human beings. A few claim to be great hunters, though some in this category shoot crippled deer and other wheelchair-bound game animals.

Well, sports fans, this tale is about that great outdoorsman and big-time game hunter of crippled and homeless animals.

One day while lounging at his estate known as the Pauly Pavilion, our Sultan of the Safari was staring out his palatial palace window and saw a fox basking in the sun by his pond. Feeling his oats, the gritty gamesman grabbed his trusted weapon equipped with a sniper scope and took aim at this friendly fox.

The hardy hunter took aim on his prey as visions of taxidermy danced in his head. He controlled his breathing and carefully squeezed the trigger on his rifle. Slowly and slowly the pressure built on the trigger until the rifle fired, the bullet heading towards its target with nothing but death as its intention. A smile of satisfaction crossed the face of the narcissistic nature lover as the bullet was making its final trek towards impact with its intended victim.

As fate would have it, luck shined down upon this defenseless creature of God and the bullet missed by inches. It might as well been feet. The fox heard the wayward bullet fly by and turned his head toward the dejected diva of the forest, smiled, laughed, and raised its paw to give the heartbroken hunter the finger.

The hunter's caretaker tried to consul the dejected diva to no avail. "Jim, don't worry, the fox will be back in a couple days, just wait and see."

Though grateful for the pep talk, the hunter was outraged that he could miss such an easy target.

Two days passed as our heroic hunter waited for his quarry to return. Return, it did! The fox not only returned but brought with him a lawn chair, a cooler loaded with Bud – which just happens to be the favorite beverage of choice for our prolific shooter – a sun umbrella, and ten of his friends.

However, the taunting didn't stop there. The fox posted a sign saying, "This miss is for you." One fox had a tee-shirt on with a target on the back; another made a sign that said, "If you can see me you'd probably miss me." They were relentless. One fox went so far and posted a sign that most of us see at sporting events, "John 3:16."

This pissed the horrified hunter off so much that he brought out the heavy artillery, his 69-millimeter cannon, and was going to blast the fox and his gang to kingdom come. Dressed in his favorite pirate outfit, the pesky pirate look-alike took aim, lit his cannon, and let go a vicious volley of lead.

All he heard was the fox and his crew saying, "Nice fireworks show, pass the Bud."

Board 'em

Well, just when you think things will slow down, they pick up again. It was a Monday night and the Box regulars were all enjoying their favorite cigars when the topic of injured ribs came up. A nameless Box customer injured his ribs while attempting a high dive off the end of a bench. He was so dehydrated that he got light headed and decided the best course of action was to go into a hot tub. That didn't work out so well. He passed out, got attended to by an ambulance crew, and refused treatment.

This nameless regular proceeded to tell his story about the injury to his ribs when another Box regular chimed in, "That's nothing, take a look at this!" This box regular, Paul, who wished to remain anonymous, unbuttoned his shirt and showed a red mark shaped like a board shaded in black and blue. Everyone thought it was a new tattoo because you could read "84 Lumber" on his chest. Low and behold it wasn't a new tattoo. Paul decided he was going to upgrade his workout by doing P-90X. So Paul, being the mechanical genius he is, decided to build his own gym equipment in his basement.

Most of you reading this are saying why not join a gym? Good Question! The answer is he does belong to a gym. The follow up question is why would he build his own equipment? Another good question! Unfortunately, there is no good answer.

It takes engineers and designers to come up with modern gym gear to be useful and safe, but our dear friend Paul resorted to

1920's engineering and went with "the more nails you put in something, the better it is" theory. Paul wanted to build a piece of equipment that he could wrap his stretch bands around and do the P-90X workout. Most people would have wrapped the bands around something that wouldn't move or break something in the house, like a floor joist. But not Paul Einstein. He decided the best way to accomplish this was to nail a board to a joist and wrap his bands around them.

Well, Copernicus the mathematician didn't take into account the amount of force he would use to pull on the bands when doing the exercise. Also, Paul thought, "Why should I move the TV to work out when I can nail the board into the joist near the TV and not have to move a thing to watch the P-90X DVD?" It's engineering like this that caused the Titanic to sink.

Finally, Paul had the board nailed to the joist and his bands ready to go. He started the DVD and began the workout. Just like the Titanic, smooth sailing, right? Not on your life. The seas started to swell and the forces of nature were taking hold of the ship. The fog rolled in and boom, the Titanic hit an iceberg and sank.

Much like the Titanic, the forces of nature worked here for Paul as well. He kept pulling and stretching the bands wrapped around the board, creating movement. The harder he pulled, the more the board moved and the nails began to weaken. Paul kept pulling, the board kept moving, and the DVD kept playing. Paul thought to himself, "I'm getting huge!" Not once did he check his engineering.

Paul pulled with all his might on that last rep and last ninety seconds of the P-90X DVD when all hell broke loose (not mention the board). The nails gave way and the board came flying off the joist like an F-22 Raptor being launched from an aircraft carrier. It traveled at the speed of sound, crashing into that fragile area Paul called a chest.

It hit him so hard an NFL Referee who was watching Paul work out threw a flag on the board for hitting a defenseless receiver. The collision knocked Paul off his feet and right on to his back.

Paul's wife, who was upstairs doing the same exercise with better equipment, came rushing downstairs. She found her husband on the floor on his back with a two-by-four imbedded in his chest. She asked Paul if he was ok. He couldn't answer because any air that was in his lungs was now on the outside looking in. He laid there motionless as his wife took the board off his chest with the help of crow bar she found in the basement.

Once the board was removed she saw the words "84 Lumber" now tattooed into his chest and said, "Honey, that reminds me, this weekend you have to fix the wooden fence. I'll be down in twenty after I finish my workout to see how you're doing. Oh, by the way, the workout manual states clearly do not use a two-by-four and nails with stretch bands, if you do you'll get hit in the chest."

So, folks, just like the Titanic, Paul slowly sank and realized he wouldn't have to write a shopping list for his fence repair since it was already tattooed to his chest.

The next rocket this guy puts into the air will be his first.

E is for Everlasting

As many of you whom have read the *Box Burns Gazette* are probably wondering, how many times can Big Rig Pauly make the news?

The answer is quite simple: As long as he breathes.

Unlike the average driver with an average IQ who knows enough to fill his tank when the red arrow hits E, Big Rig pushes the envelope. And much like his bets, he loses every time.

Let's begin this epic saga by filling in readers that one Jimmy Big Rig rebuilt an entire Allis Chalmers tractor from the ground up, with one minor exception. That exception: no gas gauge.

Why put in an instrument that can make your life easier when the alternative – which is taking a giant stick, shoving it into the gas tank, then look for the diesel fuel line to see if you have adequate fuel in the tank – is so much harder? While this worked well in the roaring twenties, things are different in the twenty-first century. They actually make gauges that tell you, "Literally, you are out of gas."

But no! That is to high tech for Big Rig. His motto, "Why use modern technology when a stick in one hand and Bud in the other works just as well?"

Well, as Box employee Sweet Lou stated, that only works if you actually have, "A STICK IN ONE HAND AND A BUD IN THE OTHER," not "A SIX PACK IN ONE HAND AND A BUD IN THE OTHER."

This reporter was told by an unnamed and unreliable source that Big Rig gets up early on Saturday morning all ready to plow his field with his big ole orange tractor when the improbable happens: Not only does Big Rig get a flat tire, he runs out of gas at the same time. The only thing keeping this from being the trifecta was he didn't get his foot caught in the cuff of his pants and fall out of the tractor.

So Big Rig comes into the Box and tells his epic story. The shocked look on the faces of the Box regulars says how can anyone be so successful, and yet not have the common sense to put in a five-dollar gas gauge. The only way we would have been more surprised would have been if one Mr. Dave Masin walked in smoking a Davidoff.

So being the riverboat gambler Sweet Lou is, he asked Big Rig if he ever ran out of gas in his brand-new Ford 750 diesel truck equipped with a modern gas gauge and warning device in the dash to let even the most mind numbing driver know he is on empty and will run out of fuel very soon, if not right now. Knowing the odds were even money, Sweetness still bet the chalk, that he did run out of gas. BIG RIG DID!

JFC asked, "What, no stick to see if you were empty?"

His Response, "F. U."

Blinking Buffoon Banned by Box

In a tight-fisted economy where every retail store on the planet is fighting for the consumer dollar, and if your store happens to get a customer who wants to spend big bucks, do you really need a regular customer telling him not to?

So in lies the premise for today's story in the *Box Burns Gazette*.

This is the city, Buffalo, New York, the weather hot but not humid, a quiet town with not much going on. The news was all about Nick Wallenda's high-wire walk over Niagara Falls when a regular customer poured water all over the cigars. A customer walked in, a seemingly average Joe with his girlfriend to purchase a cigar. He perused the store, looking but not really certain what his taste in cigars will be. His girlfriend along for the ride came into the store with hesitation on her face.

The new customer looked and looked and he eyed the Davidoff cigars. His eyes lit up and his mouth watered as he reached out to pick up the treasure of his long, drawn-out quest to find the exact cigar that will not only tickle his fancy, but keep his mind off his soon-to-be-nagging girlfriend's diatribe thanks to one Box regular. It was with such great pride at his selection that he hoisted the cigar over his head like Dustin Brown of the LA Kings holding the Stanley Cup, as if to say we are the Champions of the world (a fact in which one other Box regular would know nothing about, since he liked the Devils).

When out of the blue came a voice, which had no real reason to be heard or spoken and hits you like napalm in the dense jungles of Nam.

The voice said, "You can get a cigar just as good as that Davidoff for less money. My friend Spanky Spankowitz does it all the time. He figures, 'why by White Owls when I can buy Swisher Sweets.'"

Like Jim Pauly placing a bet at the track where the ticket taker gives him his tickets already ripped up, this poor average Joe's luck couldn't be worse. The girlfriend shot him an evil eye that said why spend all that money when you don't have to. His long awaited dream of relaxation with a nice cigar is burnt to a crisp, and the only way the agony can be stopped, like napalm, is to cut it out.

The average Joe dragged himself to the counter while getting verbally abused by his girlfriend to check out and is greeted by the owner. He told his tale of woe to the owner, stating that this guy sitting in the back telling stories about people that no one has ever heard of or cares about embarrassed him in front of his girlfriend about the money he is going to spend on a cigar.

The owner was livid by now and ready to kill. He poured himself a quart of bourbon to calm himself down, but to no avail. He then had a revelation and went to this unnamed person's locker, cleared it out, and banned this unnamed former Box regular from the Box forever, never to return or be allowed in.

As when you clean up one neighborhood, the blithe moves to another. Alternative Brews is now on this man's radar, and this reporter is one hundred percent sure the music will be all that much louder from now on.

As a side note, the Box's profit margin has increased due to the savings seen by not having to rent a rug cleaner every week.

If I were the owner of A.B., I would hold on to that idea of buying new carpet for the time being. Just wait until he tells one of your customers that he can buy the beer cheaper at Consumer Beverage, then change your rugs.

The Jinx: Mush and Jimmy the not so Greek

I'm sure everyone has had a friend or has known somebody whose luck is so bad that black cats will not cross their paths. Well then, hold on, because two such men exist at the Box. Their luck is so bad when it comes to sporting events that mirrors refuse to break around them.

The two of whom this reporter speaks are Jimmy Big Rig and the new guy at the box, Mike Spoo, whose real name is too long to write and has no vowels. The only guy who can say it right is Crantzy, and he can't say "unbelievable," and, to be honest, no one really cares.

Where does one begin when he has been cursed with not one but two mushes? The curse of the mummy would be a welcome sight compared to these two guys. Luck is defined as success or failure brought by chance rather than through one's actions.

Let's examine Jimmy the not so Greek and Mike "the Mush" Spoo's action, or lack thereof, and its effect on resident degenerate gambler at the Box, Sweet Lou.

The action on games, horse racing, and just about anything one can bet on began out of boredom. How many times can you listen to Tom Gavigan yell magic and hold his thumbs in the air? The only magic most want to see are his thumbs stuck up his ass. The run of bad luck started at the Box's annual NFL Draft party when they watch the draft, make their picks, and the guy with the most right wins.

Prior to the draft Sweet Lou's luck against Big Rig was great. One day, though, Big Rig thought he'd pull a fast one during the NCAA Championship game. Sweetness was sick in bed and Big Rig had one of his henchmen call him and ask if he'd like to bet a dollar on the game. Lou was so sick he agreed to his bet. He slept most of the day and night and didn't realize it was 9:30 pm and the game started at 9 pm. Pauly took Michigan and Sweet Lou got Louisville. What Lou didn't know was that the game was ten minutes old and his team was leading by eight points. Big Rig of course LOST.

Back to the draft, Mike Spoo was the newcomer and decided to enter the fray. He is a self-proclaimed football expert. Thank god he is not the Bills GM; this guy could pick the only horse in a one-horse race to win and the poor bastard would die out of the starting gate. Mike's pick for the Bills was, wait for it, any one of the top four QB's available. REALLY!

However, not to be out done, our own Jimmy the not so Greek, who mind you is in Florida at the time of the draft and is the contractor for the President of the Bills, the Head Coach of the Bills, and numerous position coaches of the Bills, GOT THE PICK WRONG. Could you imagine if he were friends with the President of, oh I don't know, Apple? We would all be using Microsoft Windows.

I wish I could say it gets better, but it doesn't. Since his connection with the Bills didn't help, Big Rig resorted to a new tactic: Call Lou and ask him what he likes and pick the same guy. Lou should have lied to him but couldn't. Besides, Big Rig picked that the next five teams would draft the same guy and struck out all five times.

Sweetness was on a roll, leading the entire way in his picks, as Spoo fell so far behind radar couldn't track him. Out of nowhere the Terrorist also got in on the draft party and recruited a friend of Spoo's to be his partner. The only thing the Terrorist

knows about football is it's on TV, and yet he was still in conten-
tion thanks to Spoo's friend.

It came down to the last draft pick and Sweet Lou is up by
one on the Terrorist and his friend. His confidant made picks for
him all night and advised him to go with one of the two safeties
left in the first round. The Terrorist ignored the advice he was
taking all night long and picked the other safety and tied Lou for
the win. Lou was furious and shouted, "Are you fucking kidding
me?"

Little did he and the rest of the Box know it was the Spoo and
Big Rig Effect! The Spoo and Big Rig Effect was now a runaway
train. These guys have cursed more teams than the Chicago Cubs
Billy goat, the Red Sox trade of Babe Ruth, Oakland's loss in the
immaculate reception game, and the Bills' wide right combined.

Now it's on to the NBA Playoffs where Spoo's favorite team,
the Knicks, were playing the Pacers in a final game seven. The
Knicks, up five with time running out, still lose to the Pacers. If
the Knicks ever find out Spoo was cheering like a schoolgirl at a
concert they'll forbid him to ever watch a game or say their name
out loud. When he started cheering, the Knicks missed every shot
they took. Spoo is the guy you want to pick to assassinate you;
you'll live to be a hundred.

The next night the NHL was on. Boston was playing Toronto,
also the seventh game of playoff series. Spoo not only picked Toronto, but he also predicted they would beat Pittsburgh in the
next round. The Maple Leafs were up 4-1 with eight minutes left
and Big Rig chimed in, "the game is in the bag."

Approximately three seconds after that brilliant salvo by the
Mush and the not so Greek, Boston Scored. With three minutes
left in the game Spoo can't believe his good fortune and said to
anyone who would listen, "I told you Toronto would do it."

Bang, Toronto is short-handed, Boston pulled their goalie and
scored with less than a minute left. Black magic is at work;

witches are afraid of these two guys. Twenty-three seconds left and the game was tied. It is OVERTIME. The Jinxes are still going strong. They both proclaim Toronto can still win. However, in just five minutes the Mush and the not so Greek were sitting there like the Mayor of Nagasaki saying, "What the Fuck was that?" The city of Toronto and the entire country of Canada thank you both.

The Preakness Stakes was next and Sweet Lou was chatting with the Mush of all Mushes about the horse race. He told Spoo he liked Orb to win and he was going to put him in his trifecta as a key horse with five other horses to battle it out for second and third. It was a no brainer. Then the Nostradamus of horse racing agrees with the pick. "I'm done," Lou said to himself, "I'll have to change my bet. Wait, how many times can this guy lose? I'm staying with Orb."

They're at the post and the bell rings, the gates open, and all the horses fly out of the gate except one. You got it, Orb. He is still in the gate reading the *Daily Racing Form*. Finally he realized he's got to run. By that time the race is over, Sweet Lou lost, and Orb was still running. This horse ran so long that it dropped off its jockey at a Motel 6. Lou wished they'd shut the lights out on Spoo.

Can it get any worse, you say? Yes, yes it can. There is nothing worse than having two jinxes pick against each other and you have to pick one of their teams to bet on. Spoo took Ottawa and Lou picked Pittsburgh. It's at that time the worst possible thing happens: Jimmy Big Rig yells out he's taking Pittsburgh, too. The Penguins were winning 1-0 with less than a minute to go and Big Rig yelled out, "I like my chances!"

"No," Lou shouted, but too late; the Senators scored and tied the game with a short-handed goal.

Maybe the Penguins can win in OT? Not a chance in the world. Ottawa came out and won the game. Lou can't win, and if that isn't bad enough, the Terrorist wanted in on the wager and took Pittsburgh as well.

Sweet Lou started looking for a horseshoe to carry, but Orb was still missing.

Anyone care to go to Vegas with these two?

Rumble in the Humidor

Regulars and non-regulars, smokers and non-smokers, let's get ready to RUUUUUMMBLE!

That's right, Box fans, a rumble at the Box. Let's get you right to the action. In one corner, standing five feet nine inches, weighing two-hundred pounds, and always willing to short change Nullo, Dave "the iPhone" Fiori.

In the other corner, standing five feet tall, weighing 160 no, 150, nope that's not it, 140 pounds, 170 if you count the cigars in his pocket, Tom "the Navy Otter" Gavigan.

Also, todays referee is Steve "the Owner" Dvorik.

This just in, the Otter has employed the services of a corner man, the world famous Ron "the Cut Man" Wilson. Rooster will cut any cigar, anytime, anywhere.

The two combatants entered the Box after a hard fought racquetball game where Dave continually drank from his sixty-four-ounce water jug while Tom dehydrated watching him drink and immediately began to cramp up.

ROUND 1

The Otter gets up from his chair circles the Box while his opponent Dave sits as still as a dead man at an Irish funeral. It's at this point that the Otter remembers why he got up and heads to the bathroom.

ROUND 2

Dave, awoken from his comatose state, gets up and heads to the restroom and opens the door. Surprise, he finds the Otter's hand is full, or as full as it can be. Dave smirks and closes the door.

ROUND 3

The Otter comes out screaming at Dave, "What the fuck is wrong with you?" Dave, already face first into his iPhone, is still unaware that he is getting insulted and screamed at. Fortunately for Dave, he has SIRI on his phone. SIRI shouts, "Hey, numb nuts, the Otter is insulting you." He shouts thanks, jumps up and puts Gavigan in a bear hug. Gavigan lets out a horrendous scream, "Oh, you broke my ribs!"

ROUND 4

Gavigan, being the highly trained Navy Otter that he is, reverts to his Navy Seal, Green Beret Search, evade, avoid, and rescue training. He screams, "You broke my ribs!" This technique works two percent of the time. Dave fell for it.

Lucky for him, his iPhone didn't. SIRI screamed, "It's a ruse, don't let go." Dave tightens his grip and Gavigan screams again and Dave lets go. His iPhone got so disgusted it shut itself down.

What a battle, folks.

ROUND 5

Dave, upset that his iPhone shut down and would not talk to him, returns to his chair. Tom, not known for his sense of fair play, strikes while Dave is drinking another sixty-four ounces of water. Tom pins Dave's arms down to the chair. Dave is unaware that he is pinned because he is so upset that SIRI will not respond to him. Tom begins to scream at him, "You are never to watch me take a piss again, what's wrong with you? I play racquetball with you and fill your water jug and this is how you treat me!"

Finally, SIRI is so embarrassed that she powers up and yells at Dave to wake up, "The Otter has got you pinned!"

ROUND 6

Tom is still yelling and Dave is taking it like a masochistic gay man. Dave, not responding to any stimuli because he now realizes that he is in love with SIRI, proposes to his iPhone. Our referee finally emerges from his office, looks at the two combatants, shakes his head, and pours himself another drink. I'd drink too if I had to witness this.

It's at this point Tom gets a cramp in his calf and starts screaming for Dave to give him some water. Dave realizes he has an edge, and since he has another jug of water, he drinks it.

Tom, realizing that he is in trouble, screams for his corner man Wilson to throw in the towel. Wilson feverously searches for a towel and finds none. There are no towels because they were all used to wipe up spills from Dave Masin. Then the unthinkable happens, Dave's thirst becomes insatiable and he realizes his jug is empty. Thirsty beyond belief, he reaches for a last resort. He opens the door to the cigars and grabs an over-humidified cigar and sucks the water out of it, rendering it a perfect cigar.

The referee finishes his drink and calls the bout a gay Mexican stand-off.

POST-FIGHT

Dave left dejected because SIRI rejected his proposal and made him return her to the store in exchange for a rotary phone. He is also out of water jugs.

Tom was rushed to the Box Apothecary where he was treated for dehydration by that medieval pharmacist Ron "Rooster" Wilson with high doses of hydrogen peroxide. Tom is also awaiting a rib transplant from surgeons as soon as baby-back ribs go on sale at Dashes Market.

Non Near-Death Experience

The regulars gathered at the Box to begin the deathwatch of the Buffalo Sabres season vs. the Tampa Bay Lightning in which they lost and failed to show up. The game was so boring the highlight of our evening was listening to Jimmy Big Rig tell us how he almost met the great Bud bartender in the sky.

Big Rig was pontificating on how he is home in bed, showered, and shaved by the time Sweet Lou is out of the Box parking lot. Lou couldn't argue, because he lived where Christ lost his sandals. Also, in case you are wondering, Big Rig does go to bed, shower, and shave in that order.

He can't resist sharing his tales of woe, so he told the gang his latest tale of utter embarrassment:

Gentlemen, did I tell you about my near death experience? I get ready for bed by turning on the TV and putting on my head phones – they allow me to watch TV and keep the volume up high so I don't keep the entire county of Erie up at night. This is where the problem begins. I turned up the volume and nothing. I changed batteries, nothing. And I even read the instructions, still nothing. Then I realized I forgot to turn them on. So I did, still nothing. Screw this, I said, I'll go to bed.

I go to bed and turn my sleep apnea machine on, put on the mask, and settle down for a good night sleep.

Sound asleep, three hours later I begin to dream that I'm gasping for air, drowning, and flailing my arms like Gavigan spewing Navy Seal fiction. I then black out and wake up in my old Canisius High School math class taught by the late Jimmy the Rug. My desk has signs taped all over it. One sign saying 'if you want to fail, look at my paper,' another saying 'when in doubt, don't cheat off the Kraut.' Brutal! Yes, but that's not the worst of it. Jimmy the Rug asked me what ten times a thousand was, and I, of course, smugly reply, 'one million.'

Jimmy becomes so frustrated, even in Heaven, he throws down his piece of chalk and says, 'the hell with this, I'm going to lunch with Babe Ruth and Joe DiMaggio, this kid is still a math moron.'

Suddenly I awaken gasping for air, realizing that I didn't hear anything in my headphones because I turned up the humidity knob on my C-PAP machine to one hundred percent, not the knob to my headphones.

Maybe I should shower, shave, and then go to bed.

Editor's note: This story is in memory of Jimmy "the Rug" Palisano, aka Captain Napkin. Jimmy passed away and we will miss him. He loved the Yankees and visiting local restaurants. Jimmy taught at Canisius High School for many years. He loved Canisius and turned out many productive adults. Rest well, Jimmy.

Loan Sharking for Dummies

When most people hear the words loan shark, it strikes images of organized crime, hit men, and guys who collect debt by breaking knees, arms, or legs.

That is until now, *Box Burns Gazette* readers. Yes, our beloved home contractor magnate, Jim Pauly, has branched into the loan shark business, only with a little twist. You see, being in the construction business, you tend to get people who owe you money or you lend people money hoping that they will pay you back and they don't or won't.

Well, Jim, being the math wizard he is, decided that accounting is also his forte. WRONG! Rule number one in accounting is you can't say you've written an account off and still leave it on your books if you actually never try to collect. In what planet is this accounting method used? In an effort to relieve his stress, he decided to regale Box regulars of his accounting woes. He explained that not getting paid for work that has been done is not a good business plan since you tend to run out of money and that you wind up collecting plastic bottles to fund your cigar habit.

The regulars listened intently to the plight of Mr. Pauly, when out of nowhere Phil Milanovich chimed in between his text messaging and cigar smoking. "Pauly, how the hell can you hang out with all these Italians and still talk to these people who owe you money?" Mr. Pauly just shrugged his shoulders and said they need it more than him.

Milanovich stood up, stopped texting, broke into a sweat, and said, "I'm a hundred percent Italian except for my name, and if that were me and I didn't get paid back, I would never talk to them again." Pauly began to rub his face, dropped his pizza, and yelled to Milanovich that he had given him a great idea.

The two put their heads together and got a headache. The saying two heads are better than one does not apply here. They thought, pondered, and pontificated, finally hitting on an idea that would solve the woes of Mr. Pauly.

So here it is, the plan to end all plans: Jim will call his dead beats and suggest they pay their bill or he would send a collector to get his money and it won't be pleasant.

The collector, Milanovich, who works on thirty-three percent commission, will go to the debtor and tell him to pay his debt or he would never talk to you again.

As you imagined, the collection rate is zero percent.

Brilliant!

This Birthday was NO Party

Ever vigilant, the *Box Burns Gazette* has uncovered more pages from the journal of Kevin and the never-ending saga of his bad love affair. Here it is, again presented unedited.

Buffalo, city of good neighbors. The Queen City, and apparently another city in which my time spent with a woman goes awry. It was Sunday, September 29, 2013, a beautiful fall day. The leaves are changing and everyone in the city watching the football game except me. My name is Kevin and I'm carrying a bigger grudge, if that is possible.

I just got done working the graveyard shift because one of my employees didn't show up for work, which I found strange because she works from home.

It was 0800 hrs. when my phone rang. I answered. No one was there. It rang again. I answered. No one there. The ringing continued and I realized I was answering the door. Damn ring tone.

Finally, I got my phone. Answered it. "This is Kevin, go."

"Kevin?" a woman asked. "Yes," I said.

"This is Noway," She said. I responded, "No Way!"

"What?" she asked. "No, I meant '*No way,*'" I said.

"What?" she asked again. "Forget it!" I said. "What do you want?"

"Would you like to go to a party with me today at one?" she asked. "I need a date and you're the only guy in Buffalo not watching the game in this whole city."

"I'm busy," I replied. "I'm watching Football with the guys at the Box."

"No you're not, you're watching that ABBA special, aren't you?"

"Yes, you caught me! Ok, I'll go to your party."

1230 hrs. I arrived at her house. She is waiting on the curb looking like a hold-up man trying to get away unnoticed. I got out, opened the front door. She put the gift in the front seat and promptly opened the back door and sat alone in the back. I started small talk. So did she, only it was to the person on her cell phone.

Twenty-five minutes to kick off, or the start of the ABBA Special, and I'm driving a birthday gift to a party.

We arrived. I got out, opened her door. I put my hand out and reached for hers. She put the gift in my hand and made a beeline to the front door.

She talked to friends and family. I talked to the portrait on the wall.

I saw a lonely man on the couch. It was her father. He was holding a gift. He stared at the TV. Football was on.

I sat down. I realized he was watching the Music City Miracle Game on a VCR. I looked at him and he looked at me. He mumbled, "No cable, no FIOS, not even an antenna!" A tear formed in his eye. Cry for us both, I thought to myself.

The Bills still lost that game, man do they suck! It was Deja vu all over again.

It was time to cut the cake. I wanted to cut my throat. I would have but there were thirty people looking as if their wish would come true.

1600 hrs. It was time for the gifts. The birthday girl opened Noway's gift. It looked familiar. It should have. It was the PJ's that were purchased on QVC with my credit card while I was looking at Art. No, not that art! I meant the security guard at the museum.

The birthday girl shouted, "Noway, these must have cost a fortune!"

Noway replied, "It was nothing." It sure was. She paid nothing. I'm paying twenty-three percent interest.

I took her home. I went to kiss her good night. She handed me a twenty-dollar bill and asked if I was available to take her and her friends to the airport. I asked where she was going. She said Portland.

I cried and pulled away from the curb. A cop pulled me over. He wrote me a ticket for not having Limo plates. Apparently, he saw the money change hands.

In a moment, the results of my date: I never dated again, but I did get a Limo license.

The Curse of Spoo

Gazette readers, the curse that holds the Buffalo Bills fate has been discovered. The Box's own Mike Spoo has been outed as the root of all evil that has befallen the beloved Bills. Our Mr. Spoo, not shy about expressing his love for the Bills, has done more harm than good to them. So let's compare and contrast the damage he's done. Mr. Spoo has been a Bills fan for thirteen years, and, not coincidently, they have missed the playoffs for thirteen years.

Spoo also has a great affinity for Bills' jerseys. Oh the disasters his purchases create. C.J. Spiller thought he could avoid the plague after hearing that Spoo purchased his jersey, number 21. He abruptly paid off the equipment manager and changed it to number 28. Still, this was not enough to keep C.J. on the field, as his coach claimed he was winded.

The worst damage has been caused to the quarterback position. Spoo purchased a Rob Johnson jersey, and low and behold, the Music City Miracle happened. In comes Bledsoe, and the prince of darkness purchases his jersey. The Bills lost the last game to Pittsburgh's third stringers and no playoffs. The streak is started. Spoo, not satisfied with his path of destruction, purchases a J.P. Losman jersey and he breaks his ankle in camp, has four different offensive coordinators, and then winds up in the now defunct United Football League. So much for that draft choice.

Destroying three football careers is not enough for the MUSHINATOR; he sets his sights on Trent Edwards. Edwards leads the Bills to a 5-1 record and Spoo buys his jersey. The very next week Edwards breaks a rib, can't make the Bills the following year, traveled city to city looking for a roster spot, and now is out of work and in need of a job. Way to help the economy, Spoo.

Still not satisfied with his destructive powers, Ryan Fitzpatrick is off to a 5-2 start, signed a big contract, and Spoo buys his jersey. Needless to say, Fitzpatrick went into the drink, winning only one more game that season and got cut after a disastrous next season. So all told, this man has ended more careers than any injury in the history of the game.

It has been learned that E.J. Manuel will change his number every week to try and avoid the curse of Spoo. Be warned, E.J., Spoo carries his own iron-on numbers to the game, as well as a battery-operated iron.

Non-Personal Shopper

There are personal shoppers and there are personal shoppers, and then there is Jimmy Big Rig. If you are that type of person who is too busy to shop for that special someone, fear not, for your problems are solved. Just call Big Rig Shoppers, your shopping specialist. Gifts for all occasions and problems. Yes, folks, Big Rig has done it again. He has turned an act of generosity into a disaster.

Jim, known for the time and thought he puts into each gift he purchases, will make your special occasions your last occasion. He will turn your happy marriage into divorce with one swipe of your credit card. His suggestion and purchase, a sewing machine for an anniversary gift, was for a former happily married couple. The wife, as luck may have it, is a seamstress.

He got thrown out of a well-known women's store while shopping for a gift for his wife. He annoyed the clerk so much that the local police were called. How does that look on a resume?

This didn't slow Big Rig down, as his new company motto is, "We're not happy unless you're not happy."

Here is a list of Jim's suggestion for a few of his clients:

- A copy of the bible for the King of Saudi Arabia.
- For friends of the Mush, a trip to the track with a complimentary Mush tip sheet.

- For Sweet Lou, a subscription to Ancestory.com so he can see that Nullo is really related to him somewhere.
- For Mr. Milanovich, a book on how to balance a check-ing account even though you don't have one.
- For John Crantzy, the Rosetta Stone learning English DVD.
- For Bobby T., Rooster, and Andre the Syrian, a me-morial book with pictures of all the guys who have passed on.
- For Kevin, a book titled "Men are from Mars and don't take your woman to Portland."
- A real Sheriff's Badge for Andre.
- To Tom G., the movie "Adventures in Baby Sitting" so we no longer have to hear about his 150-year-old rel-ative.

Where did he get his experience, you ask? He earned it. Those are his words, not mine.

Perhaps the best gift he handed out was to a long-time em-ployee of his that recently quit drinking. Big Rig put many hours of time and thought into this gift.

Big Rig attended a cigar event and won a raffle. He won a cigar cutter, lighter, and an object which he thought was a cigar saver. Well, it's gift-giving time and he gave his valued employee his re-gifted winnings.

The employee was stunned by his bad luck, because not only did he give up drinking, the gift his boss re-gifted him was not a cigar saver but a flask. And, by the way, this same employee gave up smoking.

The thought he puts into each gift: PRICELESS.

The Pepper Spray Caper

We at the *Box Burns Gazette* used to think Sweet Lou was one of the normal guys. However, with his latest antics, we may have jumped the gun on that conclusion.

It was a normal, cold day in November. Sweet Lou was working his usual late-night watch at the Box and his shift was finally at an end. He had injured his knee on duty the previous day and couldn't wait to go home to rest. He made it out to his car and into the front seat when all of a sudden Sweetness's leg cramped up and the pain was severe.

He instinctively stretched his leg when the most improbable thing happened: His pepper spray that he carried during after-hours at the Box somehow managed to land on top of the seatbelt latch. Yes, you guessed it. The spray went off and shot into his butt cheek. I'm sure you heard the expression, "My ass was on fire." And yes, Sweet Lou's was.

He reached back with his hand and immediately disengaged the spray and contaminated his hand. The burning was severe and Lou's eyes teared up from the spray. He went to wipe away the tears and forgot that his hand was now contaminated. Now his eyes were burning as well as his ass. Not only was his ass burning and eyes swollen, he was almost blind.

Sweetness drove to the nearest building and hightailed it to the men's room. Water at last. Lou began to flush his eyes when the worst possible thing happened: He had to take a piss. Lou was doomed. Both hands contaminated, what was he to do? He had two options: piss his pants or face the consequences of his misfortune. Sweet Lou choose the later.

Yes, folks, not only was his ass and eyes burning, his dick was on fire as well. His shift was over and he had to drive twenty-four miles back home. Lou hit every red light.

He was quoted saying, "I hit lights where I never knew there were lights. If that wasn't bad enough I was stuck in traffic due to road construction. I was on fire."

Finally, he made it back home and showered and got some relief. Lou changed into his sweats, which happened to touch the contaminated clothes from the Box. Yes, readers, his hands were contaminated again! His hands and eyes were on fire once more.

If this reporter can take anything from this tale, this is certainly it: I knew pepper made you sneeze, what I didn't know is it could start a fire.

Numbers Game

It was a cold, snowy December Sunday and the boys gathered at the Box to watch football for the day. Naturally, the Bills were playing and everyone planned to watch them. However, the game wasn't all that exciting so the Eagles and Lions game was put on the TV. The game was played in Philly and they got hit with a major snowstorm. The field was covered with about five inches of snow and you couldn't see a thing on the field. The players were like snowmen; they just blended in to the snow-covered field.

The Box regulars were mesmerized by the game and forgot all about tuning back in to the hometown heroes. This *Box Burns Gazette* reporter surmised the Philly game brought everyone back to their youth when it snowed. Everyone would go outside and play tackle football in the street. Since it was covered in snow it didn't hurt too much to get tackled on the pavement. You didn't know where the end zone was and didn't care. It was just fun to play in the snow.

So the gang watched the game and became young again. They all had smiles on their faces because they all were thinking the same thing: That it would be great to play football in the snow again. The moment was shattered when one of the Box's resident engineers and regulars named Paul came out with an all-time great statement.

Folks, you remember Paul, he came up with the P-90X Chest Board. No matter how many nails you use to secure it with, it will eventually pull away and slam you in the chest and leave you mortally wounded.

Paul was sitting next to Bobby T, a local homebuilder in the area, and they looked up at the TV and saw like everyone else the yard markers and lines were now visible. What the FOX Network had done was super-impose the yard markers and yard lines over the snow-covered field so the viewer could watch the game and know where the team was on the field.

However, it never occurred to the two NASA-bound rocket scientists this was done by the real engineers in the TV trucks. They came up with their own theory. Wait for it, wait for it...here you go: Heated numbers and lines embedded in the playing field. In case a major snow storm hits, the numbers would heat up and the snow would melt. The crowd and TV viewers would be able to see where their favorite team was on the field.

It never occurred to these Mensa members that if the numbers and yard lines were heated, how was it possible for the snow covering the yard lines and numbers to melt perfectly and give the viewers a perfectly formed view of them? This reporter is no engineer like these two claim to be, but I know that if there is enough heat to melt the snow on the yard lines and numbers, a certain amount of heat will be dissipated to melt the surrounding area and not just the numbers and lines. The two argued for a whole quarter that the field had heated numbers.

Finally the Box patrons had to conduct an experiment by gathering snow and heating a piece of metal to show the two future "Are you Smarter than a Lead Pencil" contestants when an object is heated, the snow-covered area around said object will also melt.

The two were finally able to get that the field did not have the new invention of heated numbers installed and it was in fact the FOX Sports trucks that super-imposed the yard lines and numbers.

Sports fans, don't worry about our two engineers, because as you read this article the two are now working on the colored ice in hockey rinks. How do they get the blue and red lines so straight without the colors running?

It often leaves us with our heads shaking as well, and wondering what would we be watching if these two tried to invent TV.

Country Cruise

It was a cold Sunday as usual for the second annual trip to the Pauly Pavilion. Everyone was scheduled to meet at the Box at 10:30 a.m. Sweet Lou figured he could run a little later than usual because he was meeting Marty, a friend of the Box regulars, and he knew he had time to spare.

Marty lives less than fifty feet from where he works and has yet to be on time. He has all the latest equipment to wake him up – a rooster with a Rolex, an alarm clock that automatically goes to snooze, and a locomotive that actually stops behind his house and blows its whistle. His mother comes in to his room every five minutes and wakes him as well. Yet he is late. So Sweetness figured he had time.

Lou decided this year he's going to bring his pistol down to shoot at Jim Pauly's place. Simple yes, but no. He woke up, showered, got dressed, grabbed his pistol, and was ready to hit the road. Lou checked his gun and realized the gunlock was still around it. No Problem, Lou has the key. WRONG! He threw it out because he saw it on his key chain and didn't know what it was for. He does now! Sweetness figured Jim would have a bolt cutter, so he didn't worry.

Next, bullets. Easy enough. Wrong again! Since he's had the gun for fifteen years and has only fired it once, he could not remember for the life of him where the bullets were. After a twenty-minute search he found them. Time to go. Wrong once more! He had to find the magazine for the bullets. Ten more wasted minutes, but he finally had everything.

Sweet Lou's phone rang, and it was Marty yelling, "Where in the hell are you I've been waiting for twenty minutes." Really! Here's the man who sued Rip Van Winkle for stealing his idea and he is bitching at Lou.

Sweetness finally got there and hit the road with Marty and Phil. Milanovich's son was supposed to come, but he decided he couldn't because school was closed and he felt the need to go there, open it, and study for a chemistry test. When pressed, he said "I can't go, I have to study because I failed my last chemistry test." Lou asked him what he got on it and PMJ said he got an 83. A 'B' and he is crying like a chick who had to wear a two-hundred-dollar prom dress instead of a three-hundred-dollar prom dress. This kid got the highest mark on the test in a room filled with more geeks than a *Big Bang Theory* sit-com marathon. So the gang left him.

Off they went on the excursion, and everyone all lit up a cigar. Marty pulled out his cup-holder ashtray and said to put your ashes in there. No Problem.

Well, there is a slight one. Sweet Lou can't seem to hit the holder with his ashes. First of all, you need the Norden bombsight just get close to hitting the ashtray, and second, Marty drives so fast you are pinned to the back of your seat, thus making it impossible to straighten your arm to even attempt to put ashes in the ashtray. There were so many ashes in his interior it looked like Mount Vesuvius exploded in his truck. Lou called his eye doctor because he was seeing spots, which actually turned out to be floating ashes.

The journey continued. As the group traveled at warp speed they got a call from the Rooster. No, not Marty's alarm clock, but from Mr. Ron Wilson. He yelled, "How come you didn't wait for me?"

Marty had pulled the truck onto the sidewalk in front of the Box, blasted the air horn, and called him on his cell, which he answered and resold all in five seconds and never left his seat. So they left him. They had a change of heart pulled over and waited for him to catch up and follow them down to Pauly's. Rooster followed more than half way and decided to turn around and go back home. Lou called him and he said Bobby Tesmer called him and wanted to go, so he was going to go back to get him.

As it turned out, Ron had no intention of coming back out and the next day blamed it on Marty's driving. Ordinarily he'd have a point, but not this time. Marty was actually driving so slowly now a horse and Amish buggy lapped them. The Amish dude actually gave them the finger.

Marty decided screw this and actually hit his gas pedal. Now they were drafting cars on Route 16. They actually got so close to one car Lou could read the License plate without his reading glasses and got a date with the lovely female driver. Marty was so close to her car Sweetness was in her passenger seat and she bitched at him for missing her ashtray. Sweetness wondered if she was related to Marty.

The last leg of the journey was upon the travel-weary gang. They needed to stop at a little mini market and pick up beer, crackers, a newspaper, and chips. They gathered up the items and went to the checkout. The cashier rang them out and Marty began to straighten out the bills.

Sweet Lou said, "Marty, let her do that."

If looks could kill, you would have thought Lou asked her to do addition. Then she began to stare at the group. They couldn't figure out why, until it dawned on them she has never seen three men with teeth that totaled ninety-six before. Three, yes. Six, maybe. Ninety-six, never!

So as they started to leave, an elderly woman entered the store and bought two local newspapers, the *Franklinville Gazette* and the *Springville Sentinel*. Lou being Lou, he couldn't resist and asked the woman what the hell happens in those two towns that they even have news, much less a newspaper. The elderly woman chuckled and said, "You would be surprised."

Lou laughed to himself, but she was right. They glanced at the *Franklinville Gazette* and saw a giant color photo on the front and only page of the newspaper. It was a photo of Jim Pauly, one pant leg shorter than the other, standing next to his Allis Chalmers orange tractor, a long stick in one hand and a can of Bud in the other. The caption read, "I may be out of gas, but I'm not out of Bud." They bought twenty copies, which cost them twenty cents.

Finally the road warriors got off the main drag and began up Pauly Mountain. This is where Christ actually lost his sandals. The road is so steep and goes so high they picked up a bald eagle and gave him a ride. Air masks dropped and an announcement came over the radio "please return your seat and trays back to their original positions."

There was a house built to match the slant of the mountain. Lou told Marty and Phil these people probably have never been to the other side of that house unless they have mountain climbing gear. As they got to Pauly's street they saw God wearing an oxygen mask, they were that high up. It was so bad they were higher than any Cell tower ever made and Phil couldn't text. Thank God they had a paramedic on scene.

Oh yeah, in all the excitement they left the groceries at the mini mart. Genius!

About the Author

Lou Rossi was born and Raised in Western New York. He attended Maryvale High School, and was a member of the 1975 graduating class. For college he stayed in the Buffalo area, attending Buffalo State College. Lou graduated with a Bachelors of Arts in Economics in 1979.

His coaching career has spanned the high school, college, and professional levels. He has coached at Williamsville South, Nichols, and St. Francis High Schools, and Buffalo State. At the professional level he coached for four years in the Arena Football League, spending one year with the Rochester Brigade of AF2, and three with the Buffalo Destroyers.

Also during this time Lou has been a Police Officer. He has been an officer for 29 years at the University at Buffalo in Buffalo, New York.

Cigar Boys: Stories from the Ashes is his first journey into the world of writing, and he hopes the readers enjoy it as much as he did in putting it together. His first novel, *The Counterfeit Matter*, will be released in 2016.